MY ESTONIA

JUSTIN PETRONE

My Estonia

PASSPORT FORGERY, MEAT JELLY EATERS
AND OTHER STORIES

PART 1

PETRONE PRINT

Cover design: Anna Lauk
Cover photo: Andres Tarto, taevapiltnik.ee
Layout: Aive Maasalu
Printed in: OÜ Greif, greif.ee

ISBN 978–9985–9996–7–7 (set)
ISBN 978–9985–9996–8–4 (1st part)

PETRONE PRINT

www.petroneprint.ee

CONTENTS

A Moment in Zavood   7
Helsinki is Not Romantic   10
A Less Fortunate Scandinavian Country   36
"But if You Come to London..."   46
How the Other Half Lives   53
Pakistani Kitchen   63
Johnny Depp is a Genius   69
Welcome to Estonia   78
Café Moskva   86
Choose Order!   92
Buckwheat Porridge is Good for You   102
Vodka Socks   109
Aunt Salme   117
Old Friends   129
Athens on the Emajõgi   135
Happy Birthday to You   152
The War Begins   166
Broken Apples   178

The Bold and the Beautiful	194
Playing Ball	207
Guys Like Rick	213
The Spirit of Tartu	219
I Live Here	242
Mother's Day	256
In the Heart of Estonia	271
Sass	287
The Republic of South Estonia	306
Wedding Day	319
Am I Permitted to Live?	332
Estonian House	347
Up North	359

Λ MOMƐNT
IN ZAVOOD

*I met Epp in Helsinki. Usually when Estonian ladies
ask where we met – and only ladies ask – they respond
with interest in this fact. "Helsinki!?" they say in
surprise. "Why, what were you doing there?"*

Could Helsinki really seem so distant to some Estonians? Were
they really that local in their mindset? All one had to do is take
a ferry north from the capital of Estonia, Tallinn and they'd be
in the Finnish capital, Helsinki, surrounded by *moi** and *moi
moi***. Other foreigners must have been lured to Estonia by its
womanhood via this route. Other foreigners like me.

Having met Epp in Helsinki has allowed me to extract
myself from some awkward conversations. Once in Zavood,
the basement-level bar that stays open the latest in the Estonian university town of Tartu, two muscular, sweaty, blond-
haired townies – let's call them Hardo and Janar – decided

*   'Hi' in Finnish
**   'Goodbye' in Finnish.

to make something of the fact that I had stolen "their" table, where their empty beer glasses had stood for 5 minutes or more.

"This is our fucking table," swore Hardo, clearly looking for an excuse to hit somebody, anybody. In the background, young co-eds played pool and sipped beer. The cacophonous sounds of a local rock band blasted from the speakers.

"I'm so sorry," I replied nervously, in Estonian. "I thought that this table was free."

"You have a weird accent," said Janar, who also seemed itching to punch somebody. "Where are you from?" he demanded. Janar's heavy hands were covered in dark marks, perhaps from fixing bicycles or car engines. Or strangling people.

"I'm from New York," I said, quickly moving to explain my situation, "but my wife is Estonian, so I can speak Estonian."

"Your wife is Estonian?" Hardo exploded in jealousy. He clearly didn't have his own *eesti naine**. Hardo looked at Janar as if this fact – a foreigner making off with one of their women – was enough to try and convict me in the name of southern Estonian justice. Not only had I stolen their table; I had stolen one of their women as well.

To Hardo and Janar, I was surely just another undeserving wealthy foreign man who had decided to take an Estonian girl as a trophy wife. When it came to women, multicultural marriages always moved West. Finns, Brits, Dutch, and Americans married Estonian girls, while Estonian guys settled down with Russians or Ukrainians. Or so I had heard.

---

* 'Estonian woman' in Estonian.

"Yeah, but don't worry, guys – we actually met in Helsinki," I explained in a calm voice.

"Helsinki?" they looked at each other in curiosity. "What would a nice Estonian girl be doing in such a faraway place?" Janar asked.

I thought he was kidding. But then I realized that, for a lot of Estonians, Helsinki – only 80 miles from Tallinn – was some far-off metropolis. Anyway, Janar and Hardo suddenly calmed. Two minutes later we were deep into a conversation about the challenges of learning the Estonian language.

"Do you know," Hardo admitted as we sipped our beers, "that you speak Estonian really well."

Janar agreed. "There are people who have lived here for fifty years," he gestured with his meaty fists, "and they don't even know one word!" In the sweaty air of Zavood's underground bar, I blushed from the compliment, even though I had heard it a few times before.

However, Janar and Hardo had understood that I did not come to their land with the specific intent to make off with one of their women. The first time I had come to Estonia, it was only supposed to be for one day.

Tartu, July 2009

PS. While most of the names used in this book are genuine, some have been changed to respect the privacy of certain individuals. All the events, though, are true to the best of my recollection.

HELSINKI
IS NOT
ROMANTIC

Helsinki is not romantic.
For most people the ferry docks in the Finnish capital
do not evoke the sensual feelings of the Mediterranean.

Yet whenever I find myself anywhere near the *Esplanaadi* – the long walking street that terminates in a fresh food market near the ferries that go to Tallinn – I am overcome. It was here that I met Epp for the very first time.

I had stood there one gorgeous August day, my body pummeled by jetlag, staring at this young Estonian woman and her mane of curly hair. She wore red pants, a red corduroy jacket, and orange tinted sunglasses. The little waves of the Gulf of Finland lapped the docks, and Epp had stood there smiling in the sunlight, set against a backdrop of happy-looking ships and people selling fresh fish.

"My name is Epp and I am 28," Epp said, approaching me. "I just got back from India. It's so weird to see the Baltic Sea again."

I nodded and introduced myself. Justin, from the United States, aged 22, glad to be far away from home. Glad to be far away from anything. I listened as Epp spoke, and watched her hair flapping in the wind. I watched her smooth tanned body, lithe fingers, and high cheekbones.

Then from somewhere in my body, a tiny voice commanded me to make babies with her – sorry, Janar and Hardo. I instantly felt vulnerable. "Shut up," I told the little voice. "Whatever you do, don't get me into any more trouble."

After my eight-hour plane ride, Epp to me might as well have been some Baltic aphrodite. I couldn't hold a conversation because I was so tired and delirious. From time to time, it literally seemed as if my vision would wrinkle from fatigue. Supposedly, it was 2 pm here on the docks, but it might as well have been 7 am or 9 pm or 25 o'clock. My body didn't know what time it was anymore.

And I didn't know what to expect from Finland, but I knew instinctively that coming here would be an emotional milestone. I was thousands of miles away from most of the people I knew and yet, for some reason, I didn't miss them. I had watched already as people in our international program had scurried like rats to the Internet cafes to e-mail friends at home. But I sent no messages to my friends, and I only used a pay phone one time to let my mother and father know I was still alive.

I wanted to be detached. I wanted to disconnect. I wanted to be here in Helsinki. I needed to replenish my soul, I told myself, given all the messed up things that had happened in the past year. And the replenishment of one's soul did not include romantic intrigues with anyone, not even Epp and her red pants.

Besides, I came to Helsinki not for love, but because I was in the Finnish foreign correspondents' program. I had been searching for a job online during my last semester of university in Washington, DC, and I found Finland instead. I rattled off an essay about my desire to see the northern lights, and managed to impress the interviewer at the ultramodern Finnish embassy enough that I was one of two Americans selected to go. Maybe the interviewer had sensed how desperate I was when she met me.

My life, by that point, had turned into something resembling *The Real World*, an American TV series that followed the messy personal lives of individualist twenty-somethings as they tried to find themselves against a threatening urban backdrop of nihilism and sexually-transmitted diseases.

My college romance had burned out in a maelstrom of infidelity and emotional upheaval. As much as I had loved her, the garden of love we tended had been mowed down and salted so that nothing could ever grow again. To kill the pain I fell in with ne'er do well bohemians, who ate hashish like candy. Why, some of them even mixed it in their food every night.

They were on the same sad carnival ride to nowhere as I, and no doubt as deeply miserable. Misery does love company. And what was it that that some girl had said to me at a party one night? She said that I had no ambition and she was right. In hindsight, Finland really was my last hope. It was calling me in my sleep from Helsinki: an open-air mental institution on the other side of the world.

Our program, organized by the Finnish foreign ministry, had basically one objective: to entice promising foreign journalists to Finland, brainwash them about how great Finland was, and then send them back to their home countries, where someday, when they became heads of newspapers and TV-stations, they could speak with authority about reindeer farms, paper mills, and the Winter War.

It was a smart move by a country known for its former isolation, and today I have no doubt that the effects of the Finnish Foreign Correspondent's Program are irreversible.

As the program progressed over the ensuing weeks, they would take us to the west coast city of Turku, where one could drink aboard boats turned into bars on the beautiful city canals. We would be introduced to the university town of Tampere, where we could learn to whip ourselves with birch branches in the sauna. Then they would jet us up to Lapland to hike through the stark Arctic wilderness and drink from the same streams as reindeer.

Finland, as we would come to learn, was a country where people put themselves to work with enormous helpings of coffee and put themselves to sleep with sweat and vodka. And how could I say no to all that free alcohol?

It was after a party in downtown Helsinki on one of the first nights after meeting my fellow correspondents that the other American and I took our bus back to the dormitory where we were staying. While she vomited in her purse, I became overwhelmed by my need to piss. Fearing I would wet my pants, I ran off the bus at a random stop and relieved myself on a nearby bush.

13

The night was warm and black. There was no one around. At first, I was happy about this. But then I realized that I had no idea where I was or any idea of how to get home. Helsinki wasn't so big, I told myself. Our student hall must be right around the corner.

After what seemed like an hour of trekking anxiously through quiet, dark back streets, though, I came to the conclusion that the only way to get back home was to get back on bus 55. The only problem was that I had wandered so far from our bus stop, I had no idea how to find that either.

Still drunk and incredibly confused, I met a group of young people outside a house party.

A blond-haired young woman said something to me in Finnish. Her hair hung down her back in a long, plated braid. She repeated her question.

"I'm looking for my bus," I slurred.

"You speak English? Where are you from?"

"New York."

"New York? What the hell are you doing in Helsinki?"

"I'm in the," I paused to burped, "Finnish foreign correspondents' program."

The pretty Finn with the braided hair smiled with pity and helped direct me to a bus stop where I caught another bus going somewhere. Tired, drunk, and lost, I now poured out my life story to the bus driver, who spoke excellent English.

"I used to be a bus driver in Oregon," the bus driver said. "And in Estonia too; I was driving buses in Tallinn for awhile."

The golden-haired bus driver looked at me in his rear view mirror. He seemed to be about the same age as me.

"What's your name?" I asked

"Mati." He reached out and shook my hand quickly, while keeping one hand on the wheel.

"Where are you from?"

"Well, originally, I'm from Estonia."

"Estonia? There is a girl in our program from Estonia... Epp."

"Epp. Sounds like an Estonian girl," he smiled.

"When I first saw the manifest for our program, I couldn't believe someone could have a name so short."

"Oh yeah. We Estonians have lots of funny names," Mati smiled. "My brother's name is Uku."

"Yoko?"

"Not Yoko," he smiled. "U-ku."

After a long ride through the backstreets of Helsinki, Mati finally pulled up behind bus number 55.

"This is your last chance," Mati said. "The buses stop running around this time, so you have to run and get on that bus before it's too late."

"*Kiitos**," I yelled to him.

"Don't mention it."

I made it just in time to reflect on how lucky I was to have made it. What would have I done if it weren't for Mati? Slept on a park bench? Called the Finnish foreign ministry at 3 am? When I got finally staggered back to the dorm, I was told the students had sent out a search party to find me. I was happy to have so much attention, but depressed because once again alcohol had found me.

---

*   'Thanks' in Finnish.

❀ ❀ ❀

"Do you know how to say 'Fancy a shag' in Finnish?" an Arab journalist whispered. "It's *'Halut sie panna.'*"

"Really?

"Oh yes, and "'I like your new haircut' is ..."

We were at another Finnish correspondents' program wine and cheese late night event. Was there a day that went by in Finland where I didn't go to bed drunk? The Egyptian correspondent in Helsinki, Mohammed, had also had a few too many and was lecturing me about the finer points of life in Finland.

"The thing my readers like most is when I write about the sauna," he dragged on. "You can imagine how exotic the sauna is for people in Cairo."

From the throng of other drunken writers, Epp ran up to me, giggling beside Réka, the Hungarian correspondent.

"Do you know the secret?" Epp whispered into my ear.

"What's the secret?" I asked, intrigued.

"You mean you don't know the secret?" She hit the last syllable like a bee sting. Epp then turned back to Réka, laughed again, and walked away.

Epp was weird. Of all of our group members, she was the only one who did not drink alcohol. She told me once that it was because of her time spent in an ashram in India, where people lived a "pure" life, and yet, she seemed crazier than anyone else in the program. What was her secret?

❀ ❀ ❀

Mohammed was right about the saunas, though. In Finland, our group saunaed everywhere, every evening. We saunaed in the city, in the forest, on the islands, even in special Lappish "smoke saunas," where the walls were black with soot and the air heavy with carcinogenic smog.

One day our group stopped at a summer cottage outside the city of Tampere. The men saunaed in one house, the ladies in another.

"Usually everyone saunas together," said our host Jari. "But we thought it would be too weird for you since you are all from abroad." I had heard a rumor during the program that Finnish Foreign Minister Erkki Tuomioja and President Tarja Halonen saunaed together regularly during the heady 1960s. After hearing what Jari told us, I now suspected it might be true.

Saunaing together with a bunch of naked guys wasn't exactly normal, either. We were expected to disrobe in front of what were still a bunch of strangers, and then snuggle up together on a bench in a hot dark room, supposedly for relaxation.

So what do a bunch of naked foreign guys talk about in the sauna after having a few beers? Most of the time, we were talking about what might be going on in the women's sauna. Florent, the French journalist, informed us that he was in love with just about every woman in Finland. Matjaz, the Slovenian, tried to find out which one of the girls we were most attracted to. The last thing I wanted to do was answer that question, even though I had a good idea of what my answer would be. Mitchell, the hearty Canadian, and Jevgeni, the boyish Russian, who apparently had not yet started shaving, discussed the finer points of the English language.

17

"Do you want to know the word for a gentle kiss on the ear?" Mitch asked Jevgeni.

"Oh, yeah, Mitch, please tell me."

"Are you sure?"

"Yes. I really want to know. I have a little book where I write all the new words I learn each day."

"Jevgeni, the word for a gentle kiss on the ear is dildo."

"Dildo? That's fantastic," said Jevgeni in wonder. He paused for a moment to digest the new word.

"So Mitch, if I go up to a Canadian girl and ask her for a dildo, she'll know what I am after?"

"Absolutely."

Everyone in the sauna was talking and joking. But our Finnish guide Jari did not talk. Instead, he began to stoically dump water on the scalding hot rocks of the sauna, producing powerful bursts of steam that stung my ears and made me cover my face in pain. After the steam had cleared he dumped another ladle full on the rocks. Then he dumped another. Nobody said a word. I guess it was a man thing. Nobody wanted to be the first one out of the sauna.

We all hoped Jari would eventually stop and start whipping himself with some birch branches or something, but he didn't. Instead, he kept doing it again and again, until all of us foreigners were finally forced to leave the inferno. Jevgeni, though, was the only one who seemed quite comfortable the whole time. Not only did Jevgeni not grow facial hair, he apparently didn't sweat either.

"We're Finns," Jari yelled before we got out. "It is our mission to take over the world, one sauna at a time."

Our cottage stood against the shores of a pristine lake. There was something different about the air up here. It felt as if it was kissing every part of your body; standing around naked felt like the most natural thing to do.

"I don't know about you guys, but I'm going to swim to that island!" declared Jevgeni, who ran and lept, completely nude, into the murky lake water.

I had also noticed the small island before. From the deck outside the sauna, it looked tantalizingly close. I thought of grabbing my swim trunks before getting in the water, but I figured that Jevgeni knew what he was doing, so I, too, dove in head first, completely naked.

Perhaps it would take us only 10 minutes to get there, I thought. At first, the swimming came easy, but halfway across the lake I felt my body tire, and I began to tread water just to conserve some of my energy.

The Russian Jevgeni swam strongly ahead to the island, with confidence. He seemed completely at home in the Finnish environment. With some more effort I followed him, and finally pulled my naked torso onto the mossy beach where I laid gasping for breath, the moss and dirt sticking all over my body.

"You aren't used to saunas and lake swimming, are you?" laughed Jevgeni. "It's a Russian tradition, you know."

"It's a pretty exhausting tradition," I gasped.

Suddenly noise broke our island idyll.

"Hey, it's Jevgeni and Justin!" I heard female voices scream from across the lake. "Go get 'em!"

"Some of the girls have come to our little island," Jevgeni raised a perverted eyebrow. "Perhaps I should go ask them for a dildo?"

"Who's here?" I said, quickly covering my most private parts.

"I can hear Maria the hot Latvian and Natalie the hot British girl," said Jevgeni. "And I can almost see Epp the hot Estonian from here. But, too bad, they've all got their bathing suits on."

"Epp? We've got to get back to the cottage!"

"Why?" said Jevgeni. "Are you afraid she'll see you?"

"Come on, let's go."

By now, I had come a long way in Finland. I had done things here that as an American I had never before even had the opportunity to do. I had learned to relax with a bunch of naked guys in a hot room while whipping each other with branches. I had swum across a lake in the nude, my manhood dangling like live bait. But the last thing I needed was for the cute 28-year-old Estonian girl with the secrets to catch me naked and freezing in the bushes covered with moss.

Instinctively, I dashed for the water, paddling back as hard as I could. About halfway across the lake, I began to feel that tired feeling again. My body began to cramp in pain. My arms strained to keep me afloat. My legs would not kick. And yet somewhere too close to my manhood, I saw the dark shape of a fish pass by, just waiting to chomp. I quickened my pace in fear.

I was rewarded with a cool beer by my friends when I finally reached the little sauna's wooden dock.

"You are very lucky," said Jari as he helped me out of the water. "Dozens of people drown in Finland every summer doing what you and Jevgeni just did."

❀ ❀ ❀

"What are you listening to?" Epp looked down on me as our bus drove back from Turku to Helsinki. My face chafed from the hot evening sun shining through the windows.

"It's my music," I said looking up at her nervously.

"What do you mean 'your' music?"

"I mean songs that I wrote myself."

"Can I listen to it?"

"No," I clung to my discman. "I mean, you can listen to it, but later."

"You must be the first musician I have met, who doesn't want anyone to listen to his music," said Epp.

Epp. At first she had appeared to be so romantic, but now she seemed really intimidating.

It had all started at lunch in Turku. Mitch had gone to use the restroom and asked me to order him another glass of wine. When the waitress came and I asked loudly for "more wine for Mitch," everyone in our program suddenly looked my way.

They dropped their utensils and glared, and I hung my head in shame, though I didn't know exactly what I had done wrong. Mitch had wanted more wine. Was it so wrong to ask for another glass?

Later that night on a boat bar in the Turku canals, I asked Epp about what happened.

21

"You honestly want to know?" she responded.

"Yeah, I do."

"Because you seem clumsy. You look like a teenager," she shook her head.

"But Mitch asked me to get him more wine. It's not my fault."

"It's not what you said," she said, holding her full lips tight. "It's the way how you asked."

My inner balloon of self-esteem compressed. Not like it was much of a balloon to begin with.

"A teenager?"

"You seem pretty sad, Justin," Epp said seriously. "Your eyes seem sad."

Epp's words killed me. I knew she was right, but I hated her anyway. At night I laid awake in my bunk, hungover and hot, scribbling my thoughts in my journal. "What comes next? Where do I come from?" I wrote. "I look in the mirror and see a face that I am told is mine. But. But what? Nothing. Nothing to do but slip into drunkenness or slip into sleep."

"Please let me listen to your music," said Epp again on the bus. "I really liked it when you sang 'Ticket to Ride' during karaoke hour on the ferry last night."

The only good songs in the karaoke song book had been Beatles songs, so I chose one I could carry. But I didn't know how much Epp loved the Beatles. She was one of the few who had applauded. The Finns on the ferry just stared at me when I was finished. They didn't even look in my direction as I exited the stage. They treated every karaoke performer with the same cruel indifference, even the loveable fat drunk who sang "I Love Rock'n'Roll" before me. What was wrong with these people?

Epp narrowed her eyes and smiled at me. She said that she was from Estonia, but sometimes she seemed more like she was from Malaysia, another place that she had once lived and worked. She wore colorful clothing. She had already loaned me CDs of Cantonese electronic pop and Indian chanting music with elephants on the cover. I looked back into her eyes and kept feeling that, if I looked long enough, some supernatural force might materialize. Maybe I would begin to levitate.

"Hey, Justin," Mitch the Canadian interrupted. "Got any more beer? It's hot in here."

"Sure, I snagged a few before we left," I said, reaching into my backpack.

As I handed a beer to Mitch, Epp reached into my seat and snatched my discman, quickly making off with it to her own seat in front of the bus. My already sunburned face felt hot with embarrassment.

"Give it back!" I cried. "Give me back my music!"

But Epp did not respond. She slunk down in her seat with a mischevous smile and began to play the songs I had recorded alone in my parents' basement that past summer.

I could hear the drums of the second track of the disc beating from the headphones and I knew it was too late to even bother. Like it or not, Epp had peeled off another one of my layers. Her lips curled as she listened, and I settled, defeated, into my seat. I felt like a crab overturned on a hot beach, my insides open for the plucking.

There, with nothing more than a journal to confess my thoughts, I sat waiting for Epp to give back my CD. I waited all day on the bus, but she kept walking around with the headsets, and I could hear my drums beating when she walked by.

※ ※ ※

Our group was returning from the Åland Islands. We had gone swimming on a remote beach, or what passed for a beach in Finland. The glacial rocks that seemed to form most of the island of Kökar vanished abruptly into the murky waters. I was nervous about the water, which seemed incredibly black and deep, while Epp dove in and began floating in to the distance, far from the rest of our group.

"Are there big fish in this water?" I asked our Swedish host.

"What?"

"Big fish. You know, like sharks or killer whales?"

"No," he laughed and puffed his pipe. "No big fish."

By the time our group had decided to leave the beach, Epp was just a tiny black speck in front of the orange setting sun. After my lake experience, I decided that she might get tired swimming back. I swam out after her. The Baltic Sea, to me, seemed completely foreign and a little threatening. Even if the Swedish host had said there were no killer whales, there could have been other creatures. Giant squids. Killer octopuses. Maniacal walruses.

"What are you doing?" Epp shouted, paddling in my direction. She gasped for air and dipped a bit below the surface of the water.

"I came out to see if you were ok; I was afraid you would get tired!"

"Oh," Epp laughed, as if I had surprised her with flowers. "I have to give you twelve points for this."

"Twelve points?" What was that supposed to mean? Many months later, I found out that it was a reference to the Eurovision Song Contest, an event that, at that point, I had never even heard of.

"Aren't you afraid of being so far away from the island?" I yelled.

"Ha!" Epp declared, gasping again for air. "If you don't struggle too much, the water will take you where you need to go. It's like I learned in the ashram! You have to trust the water."

I didn't like the way people looked at us when we got out of the sea. Even though we were all in our twenties, with all these new faces, I felt like I was back in third grade.

"So how about you and Epp?" kidded Matjaz the Slovenian.

"Shut up, Matjaz," I snapped.

"Aww, come on, tell us the details!"

"Give it a rest."

"Did you two smooch out there on the waves?"

"Let him be, Matjaz," the Frenchman Florent scolded the Slovenian. "Not everyone is a gossipy little school girl like you."

❄ ❄ ❄

I had told myself that I didn't need a partner. I wanted to be detached and live as some kind of musical monk. Me and my guitar against the world. Sometimes while watching Finnish TV in our dormitory in Helsinki, though, my emotions got the best of me. Each afternoon, Kicki Berg, the perky Swede who hosted a music program called *Up North*, would come on and take all the pain away. You could say I had a crush on her.

"Justin, you really need a girlfriend," said Natalie, the British correspondent, as I sat like a zombie and watched my lovely Kicki.

Natalie was a redhead from England and was covered from head to toe in freckles. She was the same age as me, almost to the day, and I felt as if she were some kind of lost twin sister.

"I know," I sighed.

Epp had finally given me back my CD one day while we were walking around in a little town named Kotka near the Russian border. She followed me and Jevgeni into a music store and pulled me aside in the classical section.

"I have been listening to this for days, and it's all really good," she said, handing back the disc. "You should know that you are really talented." I could feel the energy from her body as it neared mine.

"Talented?" I said, taken by her compliment. "Thanks."

"My favorite is the song where you sing 'hopelessly, helplessly' at the end."

"I know, I couldn't decide which word to use, so I used both," I said. That song meant the most to me, too.

Jevgeni watched us from the hiphop section with a bewildered look on his face. "Why are you two looking at each other like that?" he interrupted.

"Like what?" I said in response. I didn't know what he was talking about. Epp didn't even respond to Jevgeni. Instead she looked at me once more and left the store.

I exhaled.

At the start of the final week, we flew to Lapland. The bus from the airport took us over rocky hills through thick forests smelling sweetly of pine as our guides played for us *joik* music – the wild folk songs of the Sami people.

At a bar in little Lappish town called Inari, we danced with the local people. Later at the bar Mitch and I began toasting one another and doing shots of whiskey.

"The only sin is ignorance," Mitch said, looking me squarely in the eye. "And missing your chance."

All my regrets began to line up inside my head. Unable to keep the ghosts away, I collapsed on the table.

"Did you come up with that toast yourself?"

"No," said Mitch, swallowing his whiskey. "But I think it's appropriate."

"Now, why the hell do you have to go and say that?" I slurred to Mitch. "Are you out to ruin my night?"

"See, I *knew* it was good toast," Mitch laughed wickedly. "It gets you thinking." At 34, Mitch was older and wiser than most of us and he was engaged.

"Fine," I said, "No regrets." I swallowed another hot whiskey, slammed the shot glass down on the table, and walked outside to find Epp.

Even at 11 pm, the polar sun still shone in Inari. The thick dark trees lined a cool lake that stretched out caressing dozens of islands. Epp sat on a long wooden dock that stretched out into the lake. A biplane was moored at the end and the air buzzed with fat Finnish summer mosquitoes.

As I neared her, the tiny voice surfaced again. Make babies with her, it demanded. This time, I was too consumed in the moment to even pay it attention.

I sat beside Epp. We made small talk, but I couldn't remember our conversation. All I could do was contemplate on the force of gravity that was drawing us ever closer together.

After awhile Epp leaned towards me and pulled out a small piece of candy paper, which she folded into a miniature boat. She placed it at one side of the dock and it floated underneath to the other side, where I caught it.

"The most important thing is to trust the water," Epp said with authority. "Always remember it when you swim; if you really trust the water, the water can never hurt you."

I cupped the paper boat and stared at it for a moment.

"There," Epp said, satisfied. "Now, you have to promise to keep this boat for the rest of your life. Do you promise?"

Was she joking? I looked at the paper boat again in the golden Lappish twilight, and then looked back at her. "I promise."

❋ ❋ ❋

Our merry group of drunken journalists streamed back to the cabins in the woods where we were staying near Inari. As I stumbled down a wooden path in the moonlight, Epp ran out of the darkness.

"I think I saw a reindeer," she almost screamed, her eyes swimming wildly in the polar night. I could not understand, if she was just making fun of me or if she was really in trouble.

"You did?" I said, terrified. We had seen a few reindeer while we were hiking and they looked big and smelly; possibly very dangerous. I grabbed her hand: "Where should we go?"

"I don't know," she whispered, "maybe we should go hide behind those cabins?"

As we snuggled in the bushes behind a wooden cabin, Epp put her head against my chest. "There is a full moon out," she said as I leaned in to kiss her.

Suddenly, something rustled in the bushes. I shot straight up. "What is that? Is the reindeer back?"

Epp burst into laughter.

"What's so funny?"

"You are." She laughed even harder.

I looked around in the bushes. It was midnight, but the sky was light gray. Still, I couldn't make out any antlers in the forest.

"You know," I said, "we could just be sitting here, and a reindeer could come!"

Epp laughed harder. "Do you want to know the secret?" she asked.

"The what?"

29

"The secret. The big secret! I have decided to share with you the biggest secret in the universe."

"Tell me. What is it?" I whispered, leaning closer to hear.

"The secret is that the world is small!" Epp roared with laughter. "It's not big!"

"That's the secret?"

"Yes!"

"Really?"

Something rustled again in the bushes.

"Wait, are you sure there are reindeer out here?"

"Oh yes, definitely. Reindeer with big, sharp antlers!" Epp rolled in the bushes laughing.

I grabbed her arms and leaned in closer. As I did, I noticed how high her cheekbones were. In the moonlight, I caught myself wondering if there really was Asian blood running in her veins. Estonian? More like Mongolian.

❊ ❊ ❊

Before I came to Finland, I had spent the summer watching old James Bond films. I relished the way James used his sexual prowess to get his way with dangerous women. "Sean Connery's got his act together," I thought to myself while watching *Goldfinger* alone late one night. "Pussy Galore is no match for him."

But the morning after hiding from the reindeer behind the cabins in Inari, I walked nervously into the breakfast room and spied Epp from across the table. Her eyes locked with mine. I nearly spilled my morning coffee. At first, she looked as confused as I did. Then she winked at me. I turned and sat down at a distant table. Where was my inner James Bond in these moments?

"Sometimes I feel that she is sensitive and beautiful," I told my journal. "Her love is a center of gravity; a home. But other times it just seems too strong. It scares me."

For the rest of our Lapland trip, I only felt clumsy around Epp. I didn't know what to say or how to act. I didn't want to sit next to her, lest I feed Matjaz's lascivious rumor mill. During our flight from Lapland back to Helsinki, Epp didn't even sit next to me. She chatted up Jevgeni at the front of the plane instead. I sat jealously in the back, all alone, listening to music. I was on my own at last; a sad individual.

The days continued to drip by in pastels of northern summer twilight and beer. At our farewell dinner in Helsinki – held at a restaurant on an island in the harbor – I decided to sit across from Epp at the table. She had in her hands a biography of Raisa Gorbachev, Mikhail's deceased wife.

"I am working on an article about their relationship," Epp said, explaining her interest in the book.

I took the book and flipped through photos of the couple. On the last page, there was a photo of Gorbachev after Raisa had died.

"Poor Gorby, he looks so sad." I laughed nervously.

"It's not funny when the love of your life dies," she said.

"I didn't say it was funny." Our eyes locked in tension.

Epp looked distressed. "Let's go outside," she said. "I need to walk with you."

We left the other half-inebriated writers at the table and walked down the long restaurant steps to the island. The golden lights of Helsinki glowed around us as boats passed by in the night. It felt special. At last I had found a place where I felt I was supposed to be.

"What are you going to do when you go back?" Epp asked.

"I don't want to go back," I looked at the lights. "I want to stay here."

"Why don't you want to go back?"

"Will you just look at it?" I said, gesturing towards Helsinki. "It's so beautiful."

"Maybe you should come with me back to Tallinn tomorrow," ventured Epp. "Maybe it will help you somehow?"

"To Tallinn?" I said, looking at the ghostly boats glowing in the night.

I had heard of Estonia before. When I was a boy my grandmother had given me a book of children's stories from the Second World War. One of the children was from Estonia. I can still remember how the little girl in the book described rationing, and how she liked it when she had a runny nose, because the flavorless soup she ate would be extra salty. Whenever I thought of Estonia, I thought of this story.

One day during the trip, Sara and Florent, the French journalists in our group, announced that they had visited Tallinn. If they could go, I could go, too. I was also told that Estonia would "soon be part of the European Union" which somehow made it seem more safe.

I had never heard the name Tallinn before, and I felt a sort of unease when I realized that Estonia – this very Estonia where Epp was from – was only an hour and a half's boat ride across the Gulf of Finland. I knew the location of both places, but somehow Finland's consignment to the "Nordic countries" and Estonia's location in "Eastern Europe" kept them far apart in my head.

At that moment, when I figured out how close Helsinki and Tallinn are, the idea of actually going to Estonia revolutionized my internal sense of geography. Estonia had seemed civilizationally different. I imagined the signs to be scrawled in Cyrillic text and onion-domed Orthodox churches looking down over its cities. I imagined pickpockets to be standing on every corner, and untrustworthy women trying to scam me out of money, maybe even Epp. I mean, how much did I really know about this Malaysian-Estonian-Mongolian woman? She was a weirdo; that was the only thing I knew for sure.

As I stood there thinking about whether or not to go to Tallinn with Epp, we were joined by Sara.

"I like you, Justin," the French journalist confessed with her cute accent while lighting a cigarette. "I have to say that I usually hate Americans, but you are different from the others. You really seem like you are searching for something!"

In the moonlight, I thanked Sara for the compliment.

I sat later that night in front of our TV in the student hall watching mindless shows. Maybe the sexy host Kicki would come on soon. I was miserable now, knowing that our program was over.

Natalie the Brit walked into the room and saw me sitting on the couch. She had just gotten back from the bar.

"Justin, what are you doing?"

"Nothing," I said.

"Justin, will you just go see Epp," Natalie shook her head. "I know you want to go see her. I am sure she is back in her room now. It's our last night, do you understand?"

In my heart, I knew that Natalie was right. I hugged her and walked out of the room without saying a word. Then I took the stairs down to the second floor. I walked to Epp and Réka's apartment and knocked at the door, hoping that Epp was still awake.

The door creaked open, and I could see her eyes and her mane of hair through the crack.

"I decided to come tomorrow," I said.

"I knew you would come," she whispered. "Come inside."

All night long I stretched out in her bed, listening to our fellow program members bid adieu to one another outside in the dark – many had flights leaving that morning.

Epp meantime organized what seemed to be few personal possessions and then reorganized them again. She had piles and piles of papers littered all over the room, covered in hand-written notes. How could she spend so much time organizing?

"What are you doing?" I whispered to her impatiently at around 4 am.

"I'm still sorting my things," she said.

I thought that organizing things was just one of her quirks. Later I would find out that it was an Estonian national pastime.

❄ ❄ ❄

When we left the dormitory to visit Tallinn the next day, I kept my documents close at hand. Who knew who could lift them from my naive American pocket while I wasn't looking? The Finnish border guards gave me no trouble when we left to board the ferry to Tallinn.

Epp, on the other hand, was uncomfortably scrutinized.

"What have you been doing in Finland for 30 days?" the passport control officer asked.

"I've been here on a program," she said.

"Do you have any proof of your participation?"

Epp dug through her bag for several minutes. It seemed that she couldn't find what she was looking for. Finally, Epp fished out her wallet, and showed them her press card and the agenda from the foreign ministry to prove that, no, she wasn't a prostitute or Ecstasy dealer; just a journalist.

In Denmark, when I had studied for a few months in 2001, I had heard jokes about backward, foolish, and drunk Finns. I had even seen a few Finns who met this description. One, an old hippie named Jorma who looked like a blonde Genghis Khan, taught us a few Finnish phrases at a party.

The Danes I was with at the time looked at Jorma as if he had been raised by wolves. And here was Finnish passport control making someone different feel small. It seemed like everyone had someone they could use to make themselves seem better.

After the Finnish passport officer finally let Epp through I felt a little disappointed in Finland.

A LESS
FORTUNATE
SCANDINAVIAN
COUNTRY

As our ferry moved over the water, Epp asked me how I envisioned the Soviet Union to be.

I told her that, as a young boy, I thought of going to Europe with its colorful old towns and bustling ports and setting sail on a boat from some place like Stockholm or Copenhagen only to arrive across a polluted sea to a land of miserable gray apartment blocks and miserable gray faces.

"But it was like that," she frowned. "It was gray. It was polluted."

"But how did it get that way?"

"It took time. It didn't happen over night."

As our high-speed ferry from Helsinki bore us into Tallinn Harbor, though, nothing looked gray. I was waiting for some kind of post-communist, northern Byzantium to spring out of the wilderness – Crimea on the Baltic. But the Crimea did not come. There were just more islands and forests.

On the nautical map aboard the ferry, I read out the names of the islands. Aegna, Prangli, and Naissaar.

"Have you ever been to Naissaar?" I asked Epp.

"No," she said. "People go there, but there's supposed to be a lot of unexploded... what do you call them... they drop them in the water to blow up boats?"

"Mines?"

"Yes. Unexploded sea mines from the Second World War. Sometimes it is in the paper that somebody accidentally steps on one and gets blown up."

I decided then never to go to Naissaar without a metal detector. It was a shame that the islands weren't more inviting. They reminded me of the peaceful archipelago outside of Helsinki, covered in thick pine and birch trees with sun-kissed beaches. A few white boats rimmed Naissaar's coast in the distance, perhaps captained by those who knew how to stay away from unexploded ordnance from the Second World War.

As we got closer to port, Epp and I walked outside to the top deck. A group of young Finnish guys in denim jackets were talking loudly and drinking cans of beer. It was 10 am.

From the deck, I caught sight of Tallinn, but it didn't look Eastern. Instead it looked more like Helsinki or Copenhagen or Reykjavik. The skyline was punctuated by the towers of twin Lutheran churches, each painted a sober white. To the left I saw cranes and gleaming glass hotels and office buildings.

"It looks like Helsinki," I said in surprise. "It almost looks like a Scandinavian country."

"Estonia kind of is a Scandinavian country," said Epp. "Just a little less fortunate than the rest."

We docked and walked into a ferry terminal that didn't look too different from the one we had left behind in Helsinki. The woman at passport control sighed and looked at my passport. With long blonde hair and sea blue eyes, she looked Finnish, but there was something spicier about her that made her that much more beautiful. Now I knew why there were so many Finnish guys on the boat to Tallinn.

Her passport stamp fell and I was permitted to enter. "*Eesti Vabariik*;" I mouthed to myself. The language looked like some mutt offspring of Finnish and German, with a hint of Swedish gobbledygook thrown in. It seemed slightly less poetic than the *Suomen tasavalta*** we had just left behind.

While Tallinn's port had looked pretty and modern from afar, I quickly found that first looks could be deceiving. I noticed some nearby buildings were blackened with soot, each one of their windows blown out by the wind or vandals. Up close it reminded me of the rusty post-industrial port cities of New England that I knew from my childhood.

The surrounding architecture was even more dizzying. Here was an old Orthodox church, there was a gas station, and over there was a 24-hour liquor store, where a few Estonian punk kids with mohawks stood amidst piles of trash, sharing a bottle of vodka.

As we walked towards the Old Town, the dirty port area gave way to hotels and currency exchanges. At the medieval gate of the old city, we walked past cafes packed with portly middle-aged Swedish and German and Finnish tourists. I could

---

*   'The Republic of Estonia' in Estonian.
**   'The Republic of Finland' in Finnish.

only tell them apart by the sounds of their languages, because they all looked the same. There were also Russian ladies selling flowers, and pockets of Italians and Spanish tour groups. It was as if all of Europe had been condensed into one street.

"Do you remember any words from our Finnish trip?" Epp asked.

"I remember how to say, "*Minä olen mies*"."

"But here, it's '*mina olen mees*"."

Epp admitted that she had been able to understand a lot of things our Finnish hosts had said when they were speaking to one another. Even the things we weren't supposed to hear, like when they had complained about the amount we drank during the trip.

"What did they expect?" I was a bit humiliated. "They put a bunch of writers in a room with some open bottles of wine, and they think we're not going to drink it?"

"I didn't drink," said Epp. "I was too busy eavesdropping on what they were saying about us."

We now climbed through the majestic alleyways of Tallinn's Old Town. Its cream-colored Hanseatic buildings enveloped me. The travel guide I had in my hands went out of its way to say nice things about Helsinki, but I had a feeling that no travel guide could ever do justice to the Old Town of Tallinn. Estonia's capital looked much better.

Looking up one crooked medieval street into the dark I said to Epp, "This place is amazing. Could you imagine living here?"

---

*   'I am a man' in Finnish.

**   'I am a man' in Estonian.

"You could live here," Epp said lightly. "I have lived in the Old Town of Tallinn."

I could live here? On the other side of the world? Surrounded by these medieval fairytale buildings?

"But what could I do here?"

"You could teach English."

For a moment, I considered the idea. Then it drifted away and swirled into the Tallinn's afternoon sunlight.

"I don't think I could do that."

"Ha!" said Epp. "You can live wherever you want to and you can make friends everywhere. I have friends living all over the world."

Yes, I remembered, Epp had told me about her adventures. In India, she had helped cast a movie. In the UK, she had worked as a babysitter. Epp's stories darted from location to location. There was India and England and Israel and the Canary Islands. There was Malaysia and Cyprus and Belarus.

"I have worked with cameramen who have worked with Björk," she said proudly. "They said that she is as crazy and as absent minded as I am. They said she lost one mobile phone a week while they were filming *Dancer in the Dark*."

We sat at the top of *Toompea*, or Dome Hill, a section of the old city that was the seat of the Estonian government. From up here, we overlooked the red tiled roofs of the rest of the Old Town.

"Are you planning to stay here in Tallinn, now that our program is over?" I asked.

"No, I don't think so," Epp shook her head. "I have been here before. I am still hungry for the world."

"But where will you go?"

"I really want to go back to the ashram in India," she said. "You cannot begin to imagine how clean you feel after a week there. I need to go back."

"I want to go to São Paulo in Brazil," I said. "I want to go learn how to play bossa nova and samba." I imagined that I would befriend my heroes Caetano Veloso and Gilberto Gil and that soon I would be winning world music awards and playing on a float in Carnival.

"So, why don't you go?" Epp asked.

The faces of my parents, who only hesitantly celebrated my acceptance into the Finnish foreign correspondents' program, then flashed in my head.

"I haven't had the chance yet."

We walked up to the *Toomkirik*, or Dome Church, a place where many of Tallinn's wealthy and influential were buried in olden days. I closed my eyes, and somewhere in my brain the terrible violence of those brutal, torch-lit evenings of the 13th century Danish invasion echoed and a pagan woman standing beside a roaring bonfire screamed out "*Eesti*'" in blood-curdling anguish.

I opened my eyes again, and the 100 plus wooden coats of arms of the families of medieval Tallinn stared back at me. "Have you ever kissed in a church?" whispered Epp. I had no time to answer.

Outside, the Estonian women around me continued to distract me. There was some extra magic in the movements of the

---

*   'Estonia' in Estonian.

blonde-haired maidens that beckoned me to come into their restaurants or to buy some postcards.

Now and then a gorgeous half-naked woman, her blonde hair tossed over her shoulders, her figure hidden only by a skimpy tank top and a micromini skirt, her blue eyes inviting the most primitive feelings, would pass me by, leaving my body in crisis. I was drunk on the stimulation. I loved it.

Epp looked very different. She wore baggy brown pants, a weathered black tank top, and sneakers that had seen several continents.

In the past, I might have followed the images of any one of these other Estonian ladies into my own sensual daydreams. But Epp was far more interesting. The other women faded into the background, as lovely as the views of the city, but no longer of any real interest. My interest stood beside me, talking about the past and the future and, almost obsessively, about India.

She kept talking about Sai Baba, some guru in the middle of India who actually believes that he is the embodiment of God. It sounded like bullshit to me, but Epp did seem more connected to the spiritual world than I was.

Epp had stood in line at his ashram, she said, waiting to hand him letters filled with her wishes. One day, he had taken one. "He doesn't just take letters from anybody," Epp said proudly. "He knows instinctively whose wishes are worth being fulfilled."

I wanted so badly to dismiss it as nonsense. But I had to believe Epp, because she believed in me. If I didn't believe her, then I would fall back into the frightening abyss of out of which I had just begun to crawl. Instead, I opened my heart to the possibility that, given other circumstances, I could have been in the same place doing the same thing. I could have been in line with her at Sai Baba's ashram. In another life, at least.

"Promise me that you will go to India," Epp said. "Everyone should go at least once, because it is such a holy place."

I thought about it, and decided to trust her. I promised.

❋   ❋   ❋

"There was a giant inflatable teddy bear named Misha. At the end of the games, they let him float into the sky, and they were singing 'Goodbye, Moscow.' It was so beautiful that I started to cry."

Epp and I sat on another hill, looking down to the pedestrian walk and eating pizza, or at least what they considered pizza in Estonia. It was thick and covered with all kinds of different vegetables and chopped meat, but it tasted good to me. Epp took another bite, and continued about the Moscow Olympics of 1980. I had no memory of these Olympics. I was only a year old at the time.

Epp's story about a little girl crying over the giant teddy bear Misha brought out all the feeling I had in my bones. I put my arm around her and kissed her cheek. It had only been three weeks since I had left New York for Helsinki. But I no longer wanted to remain detached from the world. Now I needed so badly to connect.

At the same time, Epp seemed so powerful that I was a little terrified of the intoxicatingly romantic turn my life had taken. All my self control was gone. My emotions had soaked everything. I was no James Bond.

❀ ❀ ❀

The warm emotions didn't last. Just a few hours later, when I found out that I had missed the last ferry back to Helsinki, I took it to be a catastrophe. Maybe this was it. Maybe I would stay here in Tallinn for the rest of my days. Maybe this was all part of Epp's evil plan. My trust in Sai Baba's roving disciple collapsed.

"But you said there was a ferry at 9!" I told Epp. I was pacing the docks of Tallinn.

"I must have read the schedule wrong."

"How am I going to catch my plane? It leaves from the Vantaa airport tomorrow at noon!"

"Don't worry. You can take a fast ferry in the morning."

"But what if I am stuck here?"

"Do you really want to go back?"

"Are you joking?"

"Am I?" her eyes widened again, like she was going in for the kill. Maybe she was playing me and loving every minute of it. Maybe Epp knew the last ferry would leave hour earlier than she said from the second we docked.

"No. It's not like I want to go back," I said. "But I have to go back."

"Don't worry so much," she said, "just trust the water. We can get a hotel room for the night."

Hotel room? My head spun. This relationship was getting heavy indeed. I remembered something that Olesia, a Russian journalist on our program, had said to Epp when we were in Finland. "Go easy on him, Epp. He's just a young man."

❈ ❈ ❈

The next morning I said goodbye to Epp at the Tallinn Ferry Terminal, disoriented by what was going on in my life. This could just end here. I was going home, but to what? I had just graduated university and I had no employment waiting for me except a construction job I had worked in the summers off from school. And I was just supposed to leave Epp behind at a ferry terminal in Tallinn and fly all the way back across the sea and forget about it? I couldn't even think about it. Forgetting wasn't an option.

We kissed at the gate to the ferry and Epp told me that she would probably be going to London next month and that, no matter what, we might meet somewhere, sometime.

"I don't know," I said. "The world is so big."

"The world is not big, how many times I have to tell you this! The world is small, so see you in London or São Paulo. And never stamp out Australia."

The ferry ride back to Helsinki was lonely. The last days of summer had given way to a windy autumnal day. All traces of our correspondents' program, which had only ended two days prior, seemed to have been carried away in the early September breeze.

To remind me of her, Epp had given me a photo of herself looking mischievous beside a statue somewhere on the Mediterranean. I kept the photo in the back of my journal, and looked at it from time to time as our Finnair jet carried us over the shimmering waters of the North Atlantic.

"BUT IF
YOU COME
TO LONDON..."

"And where are you coming from?" the British passport control officer asked me. His sardonic attitude rang out in a crisp London accent with every question.

"New York," I muttered. He scribbled notes on a white notepad. I looked around at the passengers with whom I had traveled. They were dressed in business attire and looked ready to go to the office. I wore a hooded-sweatshirt and a pair of loose-fitting jeans. Beams of light came through the small, high windows. It was morning in England.

"And why are you visiting the UK?" he asked.

"I am supposed to meet someone here," I croaked in a tired voice. "A girlfriend."

"And is she a British citizen?"

"No. She's an Estonian citizen."

The British officer's eyes lit up.

"Estonian, eh?" he said "Is she living here or visiting?"

"Visiting."

"And what is she visiting?"

"She's visiting her uncle," I said. It was partly true – Epp had an uncle in Britain, although I was pretty sure she wasn't visiting him at the moment. "He lives in Gloucester."

The British officer scribbled notes into his pad. I thought about which parts of the truth were the least threatening to divulge if he kept questioning me.

Epp actually had been working with some illegal Estonian construction workers. If I wanted, she said, I could work with them, too. I didn't feel like telling the passport control officer about that. But what I really didn't want to talk about was that she was interviewing members of an Ibiza Ecstasy smuggling ring for an article – or possibly a book – she was writing. And what about that South London Pakistani gang she had befriended and whose houses she was cleaning – getting paid illegally, of course?

"Do you know where in Gloucester?" the officer said.

"No."

"But where will you be staying while you are here?"

"I don't know."

"Right, so you are supposed to meet a traveling Estonian girl who doesn't have a job and you don't know where you are spending the night," he summed up tersely. "Did you meet this girl in Britain?"

"No. We met in Helsinki."

"Hel-sinki?" he said, savoring the strange word. "And what were you doing in *Hel-sinki*? And – what was she doing in Hel-sinki?!" I guessed British passport control had the right to ask such questions.

"We were on, uh, a foreign correspondents program." I looked away. I hoped that the next question wouldn't be about illegal construction workers or Ecstasy dealing.

"So your girlfriend is also a journalist?" he asked.

"Yes."

"But is she working here?"

"I'm not sure."

"How much money do you have in your bank account?"

"Around two thousand dollars." The sum sounded huge to me. I had earned and saved it by working in construction.

"And how long do you intend to stay?"

"Well, the return ticket is in 40 days, but ..."

"$2,000 is not a lot of money in the UK," he scoffed. "Do you intend to work while you are in the UK over the next 40 days?"

"I am not sure if we plan to spend the whole time in the UK," I said, hoping this would stop his questioning of me. Epp and I had discussed doing some backpacking around Europe.

"Very well then," the officer sighed. He then raised his passport stamp which fell gracefully on my passport. *Entry for six months. No work or recourse to public funds* it said below a little blue crown.

❀ ❀ ❀

Where was she? I had told her my flight time. We had spoken by phone only a day before. But Epp was nowhere to be found. It was 10 am local time, I was in London, and it seemed that I had told the passport officer the truth, because I had no idea where I would be staying the night.

By the time I had walked between all the terminals of Heathrow Airport I was pretty sure Epp had stood me up. It was just a cruel practical joke that an older, mischievous woman had played on a younger foolish man. Epp was perhaps sitting somewhere in Estonia, amused by the whole thing. She had just made everything up. The illegal construction workers. The Ecstasy dealers. The Pakistanis. It did sound a little too crazy to be true.

I was such an idiot. I leafed through tabloids blaring out the intimate details of Hugh Grant's personal life, hoping for a solution to present itself. It didn't.

Half an hour later, though, as I rolled back into the terminal where we were supposed to meet, I saw a familiar mane of curly hair hunched over an Internet kiosk feverishly typing away. Could it be? Was it her?

When I came up behind this woman, I was overcome by a sense of comfort. It was Epp. For the first time since I had left her at the ferry terminal, I felt whole. Her body invited me to stand close to it. I wasn't alone anymore.

"I was just writing you an e-mail because I could not find you in this huge airport," she said. "My bus got stuck in traffic."

The same day I left Tallinn a month and a half previously, I had arrived back in JFK Airport in New York to be delivered by my parents to an Italian restaurant where I was quizzed about my trip.

My father assured me that I would remember the faces of Epp the Estonian, Jevgeni the Russian, and Mitch the Canadian for the rest of my life. The way he made it sound, the adventure had now passed and real life had resumed in New York.

From his perspective, I would soon find employment nearby, after that, perhaps in time, with my parents' approval, a spouse from the neighborhood, too. Then would come children, and then after even more time, death and burial. To me, it seemed as if my obituary had already been written. Perhaps it would even include a sentence about my inclusion in the Finnish foreign correspondents' program.

My mother meantime was still concerned about my visit to a former Soviet country. "Do you know where he's been?" she asked to the teenage waitress at the restaurant, who probably had no idea where Estonia was.

"No. Where?"

"Estonia!" my mother said, as if it were synonymous with "Somalia." She was really worried about me, but any aspect of my life was bound at this point to induce fear and paranoia. I did not feel like mentioning her how Jevgeni had invited me to visit St. Petersburg, though I had declined.

"You should come with me," Jevgeni had said. "I can show you parts of the city that are completely lawless."

I imagined that, had I gone there with him, my mother might have suffered cardiac arrest.

Over the course of next two days, the loneliness of my life began to seep into every second. It drained me of my essence. No amount of music or writing could make it go away. I wanted so badly to talk about Epp and Misha the Bear and the blonde-haired maidens selling postcards and the Finns taking over the world's saunas – but nobody cared.

I visited my friends Pete and Becky in their Brooklyn apartment that same week, only to spend a lonely night stretched out on an old couch unable to sleep.

I showed them photos of the special places I had discovered in Finland. They agreed that the sunsets and forests were very nice, but then changed the subject. And why wouldn't they? None of them had been there. For everyone else, it was as if the past month of my life had never even happened.

One of their friends was named Mike. He was a rugged New York individualist fond of mountain climbing. In his early 40s, Mike the mountaineer had traveled the globe and no doubt slept with many exotic women.

During our lengthy pub crawl together, he inquired about my relationship status. He wanted to fix me up with one his much younger girlfriend's friends. It was of no use though as my heart belonged to another woman, I told him, an Estonian woman. He nodded when he heard this, as if he had heard of other sailors who had fallen prey to the Siren Call of Estonian womanhood.

And so, I lived with the heaviness of my adventure at all times, until three days later when I found Epp's mobile number among my belongings and called her.

"Oh, I knew you would call," I heard Epp laugh through the telephone line. My black and white life exploded again into technicolor.

Our long distance relationship blossomed via phone and e-mail. Epp sent me drafts of science fiction stories about nuclear wars and gods and angels. I shared with her my love of emotional landscapes and world music.

During this time, I kept listening to one cassette she gave me. It was pop music sung in Hindi, and I let my imagination go, thinking that life with Epp would be like one of those vibrant Bollywood films they played in the Indian restaurants in New York. So much brighter; so much more exciting; so much better than anything anyone else could offer me.

My parents perhaps sensed me slipping away.

"What happened to that nice girl you used to date? The one in Oregon?" my father said to me one night in the car.

"Yes, she was very nice," said my mother.

"We broke up," I answered.

"But she was really pretty," my mother said.

"I thought you didn't like her because she lived so far away," I said back.

"I know," said my father, "but Oregon isn't *that* far away, is it?"

During our many e-mails and phone calls, Epp and I had talked of more serious matters. Epp was going to London and she thought I would like it, too. "But if you come to London..." she would ask, over and over again. It seemed as farfetched as going to Tallinn, but Tallinn had changed everything. Maybe London would change it even more, for the better.

Three weeks after our trip ended, Epp moved to London and told me stories late at night on the phone about her globe-hopping existence. I thought it over from my bed, looking out a window into the cold, October air. From somewhere inside me, 007 resurfaced.

HOW THE OTHER HALF LIVES

"Thornton Heath," said the engineer. We exited the train and I pulled my heavy bag across the gap onto the platform. As I stood up, I felt the top of my head hit something heavy and sharp. I reached up to feel the bump, and felt a hot trickle of blood.

"Hey, watch out for that sign, mister!" yelled two Jamaican ladies with dreadlocks as they walked by us on the platform.

"I hit my head!" I cried back at them in a daze.

"Mister, from the looks of it, your head is full of bread. Mmm hmm. Full of bread," the Jamaican harpies snapped in unison.

"Do you have a tissue?" I asked Epp. The blood continued to run down my scalp.

"No," she felt around in her pockets.

"Ok," I said, reaching down for my bag. I hope that I don't have to go to the hospital, I thought as I rummaged for something that could stop the bleeding. Finally, I grabbed a black sock and put it on the wound. And there I stood on a train platform full of Jamaicans in south London holding a sock on my head. I had been awake for more than 24 hours straight.

The road beside the tube was called 'Whitehorse.' It led past supermarkets with special deals on Chicken Tikka and Bangladeshi fresh food stores right up to the doorway of a nondescript gray house in a patch of the city called Thornton Heath.

The only thing I knew about Thornton Heath is that it was near the city of Brixton, immortalized in The Clash's ode to gangsters, "Guns of Brixton."

When they kick in your front door/ How you gonna come?/ With your hands on your head or on the trigger of your gun?

I imagined there were dangerous blunt-smoking Rastafarians nearby who were just waiting for an opportunity to cut up some American.

Thornton Heath was a mixture of West Indians, working class English, and East European workers of uncertain legal status. There would be no worries about the contents of my bank account, as we would be staying with this latter group of locals.

Epp had found us a cheap place to stay in a house where most of the other boarders were Lithuanians working as waiters and movers all over London. The landlord was a Russian guy who appeared to be in his mid-20s. For all I had heard about animosity between Lithuanians and Russians, everybody in this house seemed to get on like old friends.

I had a hard time figuring these Lithuanians out. They mostly kept to themselves, and their language of choice for communicating with Epp was Russian, not English, even though we were in the land of William Shakespeare.

I had to wonder at the strange twist my life had taken: just months before I was sharing a bathroom with economics majors at a university in Washington, DC. Now, I was sharing a bathroom with a bunch of Lithuanian builders in South London.

Only one of our neighbors was not Lithuanian. He was from Russia, though he could have been Ukrainian or Belarusian for all I knew. He was tall and resembled Dolph Lundgren, Rocky Balboa's Soviet opponent in *Rocky IV*. One day he knocked at our door.

"*Nuuzhna nozh,*" he slurred, it seemed, almost through his nose. He held out his enormous hand as if he wanted something.

"What?" I stared back at him. "What do you want?"

"*Nuuzhna nozh,*" he repeated. "*Nozh.*"

Epp stepped in from the other side of our room. We had just finished eating breakfast.

"I think he wants one of the knives we took from the kitchen," she said, then chirped to him in Russian. The Russian thanked us for the knife with a smile and went on his way.

"*Nuuzhna nozh,*" I said.

"Congratulations," Epp said. "You just learned some Russian. It means: 'I need a knife.'"

"That phrase will come in handy one day," I said, "along with the one people used to say to Jevgeni all the time, what was it?"

"*Zatknis**?"

---

*   'Shut up!' in Russian.

"Yes. *Zatknis! Nuuzhna nozh!*" I imitated our neighbor.

"These are very useful phrases," Epp grinned.

The same morning we took the train north into central London where we met up with a pair of Estonians that Epp had befriended, Janek and Margus, two builders.

In central London, we saw Big Ben and the parliament and the Tower Bridge. I had seen these landmarks so many times in films, and yet here I was standing beside them in the October sun. Epp and I kissed beneath a monument to British naval hero Horatio Nelson. We bought Cornish pasties beside Buckingham Palace.

Epp had gotten some extra money from working with Janek and Margus by distributing flyers for their "Proffessional Building Service".

"I told them 'professional' was spelled with one 'f', but they didn't believe me," Epp shook her head.

We met them outside Victoria Station. Both Janek and Margus were as tall as me, though Janek seemed twice as wide and about a thousand times as strong. His head was the size of a mailbox. When he smiled, I noticed that half of his teeth were missing, even though he couldn't have been more than 30 years old. His skin was pale, his eyes a light, sea blue.

Margus was a bit slighter and had dark hair and seemed agile, as if he were up for anything. Both led double lives as foreign workers in the UK and regular mates in Estonia where they had held a variety of odd jobs.

In Tallinn, Janek had sold plumbing supplies. Margus had modeled denim jackets. As builders in London, the money they made went home to their Estonian fiancées, investments for a future of improving living standards. Janek and Margus were in London because there was work and they were willing to do it for a reasonable price. These were the kind of sketchy characters who no doubt aroused the interest of British passport control. They were now part of my extended London network.

After a few *tere*'s, Janek and Epp calmly discussed – for Estonians didn't seem to argue – some financial issues about the "Proffesional Building Service", while Margus informed me that he had seen two people making love in an alley the night before in plain sight of all the Estonians and Rastafarians and working class English of London. About this, he was still excited.

We walked together through a few neighborhoods to an appealing street of brick apartment buildings, then took an elevator to the top floor of a building, turned down the hall, walked through a doorway, and entered an apartment where it seemed every other Estonian in London was seated at a table and eating a dinner of spaghetti and butter. For an Italian-American boy, watching Estonians kill good pasta that way was sacrilege, but we were in London, anyway, where they all probably drenched their spaghetti in ketchup or mayonaisse or vinegar or something even more gross.

The head cook, who was hunched over the sink straining out another pot full of pasta was an enormous man named Valdek who looked like two Janeks put together. Like Janek, his skin was almost translucent and his eyes were the lightest of blues. It seemed as if these Estonians were some variety of

---

*   'Hello' in Estonian.

albino or Viking. Valdek seemed older, and I was told later that he had a wife and children at home in Estonia.

I shook the hands of around half a dozen or so people whose names I will never remember – young women who worked in hotels, young men who worked as builders, and then I was taken to the backroom, where I met a professional-looking gentleman of about 25 named Priit.

Priit sat in a business-like chair in front of a computer with his legs folded. In the corner stood a middle-aged man dressed from head to toe in denim. When we walked in, Priit exchanged some money with the man and was thanked before the guy and his jeans jacket left the room.

Unlike the Lithuanians' headquarters in Thornton Heath, the Estonians' pad near Victoria Station wasn't too shabby. Priit's room was decorated with new, white office furniture. His bookshelves were filled with glossy coffee table books. His desktop computer looked top of the line and was hooked up to a number of equally impressive scanners and printers. Next to one mirror on the opposite side of the room hung four passport photos – from this, I deduced the source of this young man's affluence. Priit was in the business of making fake IDs – and he was open about his convictions.

"I should be able to go wherever I want to go," he explained while frequently refreshing his computer screen to check for new e-mails. "Who are they to tell me where on the planet I can go and for how long?"

I had no real response for Priit. While I respected these kinds of philosophical arguments, those British and Finnish passport controls did seem really intimidating. Priit made a good case, though, and in excellent London English. "Anyway," he chuckled while refreshing his computer screen, "passports are really easy to make."

"But aren't you scared you'll get caught?" I asked.

"Well, that's part of the risk of the job, but I don't do business with just anybody off the street," he said. "I hope the bastards don't find out about me." He then made a spitting sound, peh-peh-peh, over his shoulder.

"What was that?" I asked in surprise.

"What was what?" Priit answered.

"That sound. You spit on your shoulder."

"What sound?" Priit smirked.

"It means good luck," Epp said. "It's like tossing a pinch of salt over your shoulder. Like this, peh-peh-peh." She sucked in as she said it.

I tried to imitate them, but Priit said I did it all wrong.

Most of the conversation between Epp and Priit hummed along in Estonian, which sounded like no language I had ever heard before. There were few Germanic or Latinate signposts to even suggest what the conversation was about.

A house in German, for example, was *haus*. But in Estonian it was *maja*. A beer in Italian was a *birro*. In Estonian, they called it *õlu*.

Epp, an experienced journalist, tossed questions to Priit who, arms folded, responded with the demeanor of an expert. I assumed she was asking him about his life as a passport forger, and Priit made it clear that passport forgery was a fine art.

Rarely did the volume level of their conversation rise above a whisper. Sometimes, to my amazement, Priit or Epp would suck in air as they talked, giving their voices a tight, windy sound. I'd never met people before who spat in the air and inhaled while they spoke.

Suddenly, in the distance fireworks exploded over the Thames. The loud explosions echoed off the buildings and sounded like gun shot reports.

"What was that?" I asked.

"It's those *niggers* across the river," Priit snarled. "Guy Fawkes Day is coming up and they are setting off fireworks all the time."

I nodded my head, but I was shocked by Priit's use of what Americans call the "the N word." I hadn't really heard it used that casually in the US, but some Europeans seemed to have no qualms about dropping that ugly word.

I was disappointed when I heard Priit say that word because, up until this point, I found him to be charismatic and likable.

He was like an Estonian Robin Hood, providing documentation to the undocumented so that they could send home money to their wives and kids. And who was that bastard passport control officer to stand between a family man like Valdek and his paycheck?

"Kissing British passport control's arse," Priit said, "is against my principles."

"Priit," I asked during a lull in the conversation. "What is your last name?"

"Kõrvits," he said. "It means pumpkin."

"Korvits," I tried.

"No, no, Kõrvits," Priit said again, putting the stress on the first vowel, which sounding tight, somewhere between the 'o' in 'open' and the 'o' in 'option.'

"Kööörvits," I said, making another attempt at this odd-sounding 'õ' vowel. From the bemused looked on Priit's face, I had screwed it up again.

"It's ok if you can't say it," said Epp to comfort me. "You sound like you are from our biggest island, Saaremaa. They also say 'ö' instead of 'õ.'"

Those two sounds seemed almost identical to me, but the thought of sounding like a native son of one those pretty Baltic islands restored my confidence.

"How do you say '"Mr." in Estonian?" I asked Priit.

"*Don*," Priit chuckled in response.

"You mean your father is '*Don* Kõrvits'?" I said in disbelief. It sounded like something out of *The Godfather*, but Epp did not interrupt to correct Priit.

"Exactly," Priit laughed harder, wiping some tears from his eyes, "And I am Don Kõrvits as well."

"Well, Don Kõrvits," I said, extending my hand, now laughing too. "It's been a pleasure to meet you." Priit told us we could visit anytime, and Epp said we would meet again.

Outside the apartment, Epp set me straight.

"Priit was just having a bit of fun," she said. "We don't say '*Don*', we say '*Härra*.'"

"Well, Priit does say *nigger*."

"Oh, we have this problem in Estonian," Epp sighed. "Our word for a black person is *neeger*."

"So why don't you just change it to the word for "black' instead?" I said.

"No, that's even worse," she said. "The word for black is the same in Estonian as the word for dirty."

"What about the word for African?"

"*Afrikaanlane*?"

"That sounds good. You could use that one. It reminds me of a reggae song: *No matter where you come from/ If you are a black man/ You are an African.*"

Epp looked at me as if I was nuts.

"I don't think Estonians are going to stop saying *neeger,*" she shrugged as we walked into the tube station. "They are not so politically correct."

PAKISTANI
KITCHEN

---

*When two people are forced to share one room in
a house of Lithuanians in South London, they are
bound to learn quite a bit about each other in
a relatively short amount of time.*

We would stay up late into the night after all the Lithuanians
went to sleep. Usually we would lie on the floor, looking at the
ceiling and plotting our future. Maybe we would go to Chile
or China or India. And never stamp out Australia. When we
got tired of planning, Epp would jot down notes in her notebook and I was finishing up the final chapters of Jack Kerouac's
Dharma Bums.

The mornings were different. By now, it was late October
and one could barely tell what time it was based on the milky
gray light that accounted for morning in England.

I would sleep with the covers wrapped tightly around me in
our tiny, cold room, while Epp would crack open an eye, catch
the time from a travel alarm clock, and explode out of the bed in

a race to the kitchen, where she would use a kettle (that looked as if it had never been washed ever) to heat up two "students' coffees" – made by dumping a spoonful of ground coffee into the bottom of a cup, followed by the boiling water and then some milk.

She would then stride back into the room, and help me to dump the coffee down my tired throat. I thought that one cup a day was the rule, but Epp would have one for breakfast and one at lunch and then maybe one in the afternoon. She was a real addict. "I'm going trying to cut down but, you know, it's normal in my country," she had said. "Estonians really like coffee, we and Finns are the biggest coffee drinkers in the world."

After her first dose in the morning, she would usually announce the options for the day's plans. Epp always had plans, and would slip into depression should she not check some mental box. Once we were late for a train into the central London and she flew into a quiet rage.

"I wanted to get there by 11!" she stormed.

"Don't worry, we can take the next one," I said.

"But the next one comes in 30 minutes!"

"So what? We can go back to the kiosk and read about Hugh Grant and Kylie Minogue's personal lives. Maybe George Michael has been arrested in another men's bathroom."

Epp did not find me funny. Instead, she pouted alone on a nearby bench. She had planned to get into London by a certain time. Her whole day had been thrown into turmoil by missing one little northern-bound train.

These rigid schedules and this obsession with time annoyed me, although Epp assured me that this is very normal in her country where everyone has plans and no one is ever late. And I knew myself that without Epp I would still be in bed somewhere, with no idea what to do next, sleeping off a hangover.

One day we went to Croydon, a London suburb located south of Thornton Heath. Our destination was the home of a Pakistani man, a single father and businessman named Mustaq. Epp had met the mysterious Mustaq on the street, gotten in a conversation with Mustaq's little son and, in what was either extreme naivety or the spirit of a true adventurer, she had agreed to come to their house and organize it. You see, Epp liked to organize things.

As we caught the train south to Mustaq's home, Epp related his life story to me. Mustaq had been born in Pakistan but had come to London seeking work where he had fallen in love with an English woman, Polly. Polly had borne him a son, but eventually turned to heroin for consolation from the British weather. So now, Mustaq – born in the spiritual, sun-baked land of Pakistan – raised his son alone in a grimy, Godless London suburb while his wife came and went, continuing her awful habit elsewhere.

Epp also told me one other thing about Mustaq. He hated America and Americans. He was almost going to give me a ride from Heathrow on my first day, but when he learned that the woman he had invited in to spruce up his life for a few quid was dating a citizen represented by President George Walker Bush, he refused.

"I thought you said he was from Estonia," Mustaq had said, banging his fist on the table.

"No, he's from New York."

"Then I will not pick him up," he had said, disgusted by the idea. "Helping an American is against my principles."

Epp had taken the bus to the airport instead.

Later, Epp tried to persuade Mustaq that I did not like President Bush nor was I fond of American policies in the Middle East, and this eventually enabled him to at least hesitantly welcome me into his house.

We had left the Croydon station and walked through a semi-run-down neighborhood to a line of row houses, then up a flight of stairs into Mustaq's South London oasis. The dimly-lit home was full of noisy Pakistani men on their way to a flight back to Islamabad. I shook each of their hands and wished them safe flights.

The house itself was different from the others next to it. This house had no grass in the front yard and the entrance stunk like an Indian restaurant. The hallway was filled with piles of black shoes – Mustaq had many visitors, some of whom who stayed to work illegally.

I knew, and they knew, that because of the global situation we in some ways could not really be open with one another. The certainty of a potential American-led invasion of Iraq drew ever closer, and it seemed that every month some poor Westerner was having his head lopped off by Jihadists and broadcast on the Internet.

A cute Estonian girl like Epp was of no threat and was to be treated well in Mustaq's house. An American from New York was a different story.

Mustaq said little as he put out delicious food of lamb, rice, and pitas on the table, leftovers from these men's pre-flight meal. The Pakistani was short with dark eyes. He wore a base-ball cap, and I could barely see his face. Around his neck was hung a heavy gold chain.

We studied each other from across the table, but said no-thing, not even making eye contact. I didn't want to talk to him about the Palestinians or September 11 or beheadings.

"This food is great," I said, breaking the silence. "How do you make it?"

"This is nothing," he said quietly, "compared to what those men just ate."

Epp began to chat with him about what work needed to be done at the house next day. His thoroughly Anglicized 10 year old son spoke with us at the same time from behind spectacles in proper British English about the plot twists of the most re-cent *Harry Potter* book.

"So, when do you think the war will begin in Iraq?" Mustaq said to me at last. He looked down at his hands.

"I hope it doesn't begin."

"Oh, it will begin. The Americans are already moving the army there."

"Well, I sent letters to my senators asking them not to sup-port it," I said, "but they didn't agree with me."

Mustaq cracked his knuckles.

"There is nothing we can do to stop this," he said. "That is why I am here in London. All my relatives ask when I am com-ing back. But the truth is that I am never going back." He looked me in the eyes from beneath his cap, and then eyed his hands again. After eating, Mustaq told Epp and me that to earn a few extra pounds we could help distribute some flyers for his taxi service. The flyers were in the taxi business' office down the street. We thanked him for the food and made our way back into the gray and wet London evening, arriving at a white building with glass windows, through which I could see about 20 Pakistani men sitting around eating kabobs and watching Al-Jazeera on a big-screen TV. Coalition war planes had recently bombed an Afghan village by accident.

The men welcomed Epp into the room and gave her boxes of the flyers we were to distribute. The room smelled of Middle Eastern spices and body odor. The windows dripped with condensation.

"Where are you from?" asked one merry Pakistani man while shoving humus-caked pita bread into his mouth.

"Estonia," said Epp freely.

"And you," he said pointing at me, "Where are you from?"

I said nothing, afraid of announcing my American citizenship to this room full of guys.

"He looks like he's from Poland," laughed another fat, bearded Pakistani cab driver.

"That's right," I muttered. "Poland."

JOHNNY DEPP
IS A GENIUS

In the end, it turned out that what I told the British passport control officer had been the truth. I would not spend my enormous treasure of two-thousand American dollars in Great Britain. We would go to Italy instead.

One evening, though, Epp approached me, looking a bit concerned.

"What is today's date?" she asked, biting her lip.

"I think today is November 6th," I said. I checked our mobile phone. "Yep, it's the 6th."

"Oh, I thought all the time that the 6th is tomorrow. I thought that Wednesday is the 6th, you know."

"No, tomorrow is the 7th."

"Please don't be mad at me," Epp said, pulling out the plane tickets. "But our flight to Rome left this morning."

I wasn't mad at Epp. I could have made the same mistake myself. Besides, the tickets only cost us 15 pounds total on the legendary low-cost airline Ryanair. Epp had bought the tickets some weeks ago and kept telling me that we have to fly out on first Wednedsay of November. The only problem was, as I came to find out, Epp had a hard time keeping track of days, months, even years.

"I think we should go to the airport to see if they would honor our tickets anyway, even if we are 24 hours late," I finally decided.

"Maybe they won't notice?" Epp plotted as we packed our things. "Or maybe we'll show up, and act like it is the 6th. They will tell us it isn't, but we will act surprised, and they will let us on anyway," she said.

After a manic night of packing and scheming, we were about to exit our Thornton Heath abode, when one of the Lithuanians stopped us.

"Where are you going?" he said. "You just got here. You have lived here for what, three weeks only?"

"We were just on vacation," I said, walking towards the door. And that's what it was, though most people came to England to see the Tower of London and go shopping in Carnaby Street. I had spent my nights in an unheated room in South London in a house shared with a bunch of illegal Lithuanians instead.

"Vacation?" The Lithuanian was puzzled.

"Yep. What about you? What are your plans?" I asked.

"Well, I am going to stay here for a year or two and make some money," he said. "Then we are going to America. That's where the real money is."

I thought of his words on the way to the airport.

* * *

"Just stay here, I'll handle this." I left Epp and our belongings beside a window in the Ryanair terminal and approached the desk for the Rome flight.

"I'm sorry, sir, can I help you?" asked the Ryanair representative. Her name tag said Laurie, and she was heavy set and very British. I assumed that she had eaten a lot of fish and chips in her life.

"Yes, I just wanted to check in for the flight to Rome."

"Ok, can I see your tickets?"

"Sure." I handed them to her.

"Sir, this flight left yesterday. These tickets are for the 6th. Today is the 7th."

"It *is*? No way!" I tried to sound as suprised as possible.

"Yes, sir, I'm sorry, but you missed your flight."

"Well, can you just put us on the one for today?"

"No, these tickets are nonrefundable and nontransferable."

"But we paid for tickets to Rome and you're not going to honor that?"

"I can't change these tickets, sir."

"But we paid you money, and for this money we get nothing?" I stammered. "Where are we going to go then? We're supposed to be in Rome!"

"Sir, today's flight is full," Laurie demurred, "but maybe if you wait another 24 hours, we can see if there are seats for on tomorrow's flight that you could *purchase*, sir"

"24 hours? Let me talk it over with my girlfriend."

I walked over to Epp and told her the news. "Maybe we should just spend the evening at the airport and get on the next flight?" I said to her. In fact, we already had made sandwiches for such a scenario. We could just sit around and write in our journals and talk: paradise.

"Let's think about this some more," she said. "We do have a full day ahead of us."

We sat for awhile reading our books. But Epp started to get itchy. "Why should we stay overnight in the airport while there are so many planes leaving right now?" she argued. "And why the heck should we go Rome at all while there are so many other directions available?"

As I finished the last pages of *Dharma Bums*, Epp started walking from booth to booth looking for the next, cheapest available flight to whatever place seemed remotely interesting. But what about our return ticket to London from Venice? That was a factor too. We obviously had to go somewhere that would bring us closer to the floating city.

After some time, Epp hustled back to me.

"There is a flight to Lyon boarding in half an hour," she said out of breath. "We could get on it for 50 euros!"

"That's great, but where is Lyon?"

"In France!"

"France?" I had never been to France. And it wasn't Paris, which made it seem less threatening.

"That sounds good," I said, tucking my book into my backpack. "Let's go."

By nightfall we had flown to France and used our rudimentary French skills to secure an attic-level room with a skylight in a hostel in central Lyon. As the rain poured down on the sky-light, we fell asleep in each other's arms.

The next day we took a train to Grenoble, a romantic university town at the foot of the French Alps. It was the weekend, and the locals had come from the countryside on this weekend to sell us fresh bread and huge blocks of smelly cheeses and elegant yet dirt-cheap wines.

I had read in an article that the actor Johnny Depp had married a French singer and moved to the south of France, where he sipped wines and ate smelly cheeses and reviewed scripts for pirate movies from his sunny villa. As we strolled along the mountainside streets of Grenoble, I realized why a person could spend eternity here in Europe. *Johnny Depp*, I thought, *is a genius.*

Epp meantime had started to teach me Estonian. I had insisted because I felt that our relationship would be unequal if only she learned my language and I didn't learn hers. Our relationship would require this balance for us to truly be happy, I thought. Otherwise she would always be working harder to please me.

I was convinced that I could learn Estonian. It would be just like learning the guitar; at first I was horrible, but eventually I was jamming along with the Rolling Stones. I believed in my bones that, if I applied myself, Estonian would come eventually. These things took time.

Epp, now my private tutor, rattled off the names of various familiar things. She taught me the present and past tenses, and told me that the Estonian language had no future tense or gender, which made me very happy. Sometimes, when she woke up in the morning, she would start speaking to me in Estonian. Then her eyes would focus, and she would realize that I didn't understand a word she had said.

We traveled like this for days. We took an overnight train into Italy, where Epp's dirty blond curls aroused the interests of the Italian men, who would wink at her and cry: "*Che bella, che bella!*"*

"*Questa e mi fianzata,*" I would yell back at them, "This is my fiancée." It wasn't true. Or was it? Either way, I wrapped my arms around her waist to let them know that if they wanted her, they were going to have to kill me first. Since I was taller than most of my fellow *paesans***, I didn't think they would try anything, but it felt good to imagine banging their heads together should they try anything with my woman.

"Since when did you get so macho?" Epp asked, as we walked down the lanes of Florence.

"I don't know," I said. "This country is just bringing it out in me."

During the days we would buy fresh foods from local shops and eat on old Italian bridges over rivers that looked as if they had run from the pallets of Michelangelo or Botticelli.

"Is Estonian food as good as Italian food?" I kidded her.

"Not really," she sighed, savoring a potato dripping in pesto.

"Well, what do you eat? What's the national food?"

"Pork, sauerkraut, potatoes, blood sausage," Epp said.

"Blood sausage? That doesn't sound so good."

---

*   'How pretty, how pretty!' in Italian.
**   'Countrymen' in Italian.

"Oh, but it's actually very tasty, especially at Christmas with jam."

I wanted to believe her, but could not. All this talk of blood almost made me lose my appetite. It made my nearby stash of mozzarella seem even more important. I stroked the soft cheese as if it were my little pet.

Our two-person caravan moved through Italy to Slovenia then back up into Italy, and then, by plane, via to Dublin. The Dublin flight was bumpy, and I began to calm myself by whispering secret mantras.

"What are you saying?" asked Epp.

"It's one of my mantras. I say them to myself when I fly."

"What, are you afraid we are going to crash?"

"Shut up." The plane rattled in the wind.

"Ladies and gentleman, the captain has turned on the 'fasten your seat belt' sign," a flight attendant said in a thick Irish brogue.

"I think it would be nice to crash," Epp continued as the plane bumped again. "I have wanted to write a book about a plane crash. First, I could write a non-fiction book about what happened," she said in excitement. "And then I could use the experience for a novel, too."

"Maybe you can just imagine it. It might be safer," I said.

"But one cannot know what it is like to crash without experiencing it," said Epp, looking out the window into the stormy night. "And of course it would be a happy crash. We would land in the water with no people killed, and we could swim to Wales."

"You suck."

Epp looked into my frightened eyes and I leaned forward. We both knew that the best cure for any kind of phobia was a kiss.

❀ ❀ ❀

Our trip was coming to an end, and I did not look forward in any way to going back to New York. We had taken a bus from Dublin to Cork, and I would be leaving for home in just a few days.

Where was my home anyway? Home seemed to be here with Epp. Without her? That was some murky emotional hell in the distant past. That life was over. It was the two of us now. We would have to stay together.

One day, I summoned my courage in the side streets of Cork. Epp was toying with an umbrella next to a mural in an underground garage. I was about to take a photo of her posing with it as an old Chinese lady when I asked her very honest question. "Would you marry me?"

Epp gave me a strange look, looked at her umbrella, looked at the mural, and then waved her arm in the air. "No! No!" she gestured. And she put the umbrella over her other shoulder, playing on.

I was crushed inside, but I said nothing. I waited for her, took her stupid photos and we just walked on through Cork, as if nothing had happened. I accepted her "no," and the quiet misery churned in my belly. If she doesn't want to marry me, I stormed in my head, then what am I doing wasting my time with her?

"What is wrong with you?" Epp asked, as we crossed over a bridge. The weather was moist and gray. An Irish street band played Bryan Adams' "Summer of "69" on a corner in the distance.

"Nothing," I said.

"What do you mean, 'nothing'? You've been moping all day. Why are you so miserable? You should be happy. Life is good."

"Happy?" I erupted. "You tell me that you don't want to marry me and I am just supposed to be happy? Like I am supposed to just walk it off?"

"You asked me to marry you?"

"And you, you act like it's no big deal!"

"You asked me if I wanted to marry you? When?"

"Of course I asked, but you said 'Nooooo!' because you just have to go and invite me to London and then break my heart."

"But I didn't tell you I didn't want to marry you."

"You didn't?!"

"I did not."

"But you said 'no' in the garage with the mural. I stood and said, 'Will you marry me?' and you said 'No.'"

"Oh," Epp blushed. "I just didn't want you to take my photo. I didn't hear what you said. Of course, I will marry you!"

We hugged and kissed, and my universe magically rebalanced itself.

One day, in a smoky pub near the Cork bus station, Epp asked me to write out everything I knew in the Estonian language. Epp sipped her coffee and thumbed our Lonely Planet travel book while I tried to concentrate amidst the smog of cigarette smoke and Irish folk music. Outside, the November skies opened up and it began to rain.

The short testament began: *Mina olen Justin. Ma armastan Eppu.*[*]

---

[*]   "I am Justin. I love Epp." In Estonian.

WELCOME TO
ESTONIA

The hardest numbers to learn were kaheksa *and* üheksa*.

The rest of the primary numbers escalated in a memorable song of *üks, kaks, kolm, neli, viis, kuus, seitse**. Why, seitse almost sounded like 'seven'. But *üheksa*? Where did they come up with that one?

I tried to imagine how some Finno-Ugric reindeer herders in the Ural Mountains centuries ago had found the time to dream up such long words for such basic things. This was, after all, the place where Epp's people had come from. This explained the Estonians' impossibly high cheekbones.

Estonian did seem hard, but I was not discouraged. After remembering that the Finns took it one step further and made it *kahdeksan* and *yhdeksän***, I thanked the Finno-Ugric love

---

* 'eight' and 'nine' in Estonian.
** 'one, two, three, four, five, six, seven' in Estonian.
*** 'eight' and 'nine' in Finnish.

gods that I had found a South Estonian farm girl, rather than a rosy-cheeked Finn from above the Arctic Circle.

We had spent the last of my money in London after traveling through France, Italy, Slovenia, and Ireland. Epp had come and visited me in the US, too, then left to go back to Estonia to set things up for my arrival.

Why Estonia? Epp said she wanted to finish her master's degree and I wanted to go back to the gorgeous city of Tallinn and learn some Estonian. Besides, I had wanted to become a foreign correspondent, hadn't I?

Epp made it clear though that she did not want to stay in Tallinn. Her travels were far from over. She could hear the ashram calling.

"Promise, we won't stay in Tallinn forever," Epp asked before we moved. "Promise, you would come to India with me after that?"

"Only if you promise to come to Brazil."

"It's a deal."

But before India and Brazil, I found myself up north again. Less than four months after I left our foreign correspondents program, I was now returning to the romantic city of Helsinki. Finland appeared out of the clouds below – ordered highways traveled by sleepy drivers; endless green forests; ultra-modern buildings; snow-dusted fields. Here I was again. It wasn't home, but it was special.

But Tallinn looked different than Helsinki from the air. It was under construction. Beside the new, ultramodern buildings stood burned out 19th century factories and decrepit Soviet monstrosities. If Johnny Depp had been a genius for relocating to a villa in southern France, I wondered what would be the right term for an American university grad who decided to move to Tallinn in the middle of winter.

And it was cold. Epp had shown me photos of cars buried in snow; of children forced to stay at home because they couldn't go out. School had been cancelled anyway because the pipes in their kindergartens had frozen over night. Some kind of Arctic blizzard had laid waste to Estonia since late November, and the forecast was for more ice and more darkness. This is what I had to look forward to as my marathon 8-hour journey from New York ended at the Tallinn airport.

Epp greeted me at the airport in Tallinn, wearing a white coat and white boots. Her medusa-like hair hung over her shoulders. It was an outfit that I thought could persuade any living human being to give this young woman whatever it is she wanted. She had worn it throughout her visit to New York in December. She had spent the holidays with our family and flown back to Estonia a week before me.

On the train to New York City that month, I had told Epp that I liked her outfit. "You can tell you are from Eastern Europe," I said. I had meant that she looked a bit outrageous and eye-catching, but Epp took offense.

"What do you mean I look Eastern European?"

"I didn't mean it in a bad way. I just meant that you look different; exotic."

"But how exactly do I look different?"

"Well, Epp, you are wearing white boots and orange sunglasses and you have high-cheekbones," I said. "Look around, do you look like anybody else on this train?"

We looked at the New York commuters, most of them overweight and dressed in sober, urban colors.

"You have a point," Epp conceded. "But I bought this in Tunisia. This jacket is from North Africa, not Eastern Europe!"

My plans for Tallinn were to start my elusive career as a foreign correspondent and to get a gig teaching English. Epp had already secured a job at an Estonian woman's magazine, so we were set as far as it came to our finances. The $500 I brought along from doing construction work over the winter holiday would pay our first two months rent at the tiny apartment Epp had found on Kentmanni Street just across from the American embassy.

When my mother heard that we were living across from the embassy she said it made her feel safe. She also bugged me to befriend the embassy staff, as if I would start hanging out with the consular officer and playing basketball with the resident marines.

The embassy was under 24-hour guard. If you so much as sneezed the wrong way in front of it, you might warrant the attention of their security personnel. One couldn't just show up in their gym shorts with a basketball ready to shoot some hoops.

Epp tried to prepare me for the apartment. It was a good deal, she said. It was centrally located with pretty cheap rent, but it "needed work," a coded way of saying it was a dump. I could tell she was worried that I wouldn't like our new place, but I didn't really care what it was like. I was just happy to be back with my loved one.

As we exited the cab, I rolled my lone bag over the icy curb, foolishly stepping in a puddle of murky brown ice water. I was wearing thin leather shoes.

Welcome to Estonia, I thought, pulling my soaked foot from the muck. I felt almost as out of it as I had on that train platform in Thornton Heath. At least my head wasn't bleeding.

Our studio apartment was actually better than I had expected, but that wasn't saying much. It had an ugly, broken toilet that needed to be replaced, and the faucets produced a rust-colored liquid, supposedly water. The apartment also had built-in cabinets with glossy, retro-looking doors, but little else.

Even if I had no memories of Leonid Brezhnev's stagnating Soviet Union, it lingered in the air of our apartment, in the gray wallpaper, the gray bathroom, and the gray kitchen. The Kentmanni apartment didn't even have a working phone line. Epp said that most young people in Estonia these days didn't even have land lines. They just had mobile phones.

We wouldn't stay in our new home for long. We had to leave for the town of Suure-Jaani in the middle of Estonia to get some of Epp's things that same night. After leaving most of my belongings at the apartment, we trudged over to the Tallinn bus station.

"How do you feel?" Epp asked.

"Tired and a little lonely," I admitted, looking at the cold, gray buildings.

"Lonely?"

"No, I am happy to be with you," I said, pulling her closer. "But you are the only person I know here."

"Don't worry," she grasped my hand, "I am sure you will make friends."

"Well, I'm not an Estonian," I said, looking at the piles of ashy snow on the curb. "But I'm here for the next five months.

I'll adapt." We had agreed to stay until June. Epp would get her graduate degree in journalism by the beginning of summer, and then we would go to India or Brazil.

Looking around on our way to bus station I started to understand why Epp did not plan to stay in this city for the rest of her life. This side of Tallinn looked nothing like the fairytale medieval town I had visited in summer. There were no Nordic maidens beckoning me to buy roasted nuts or postcards. There were no fat Scandinavians drinking beers in cafes. There were just gray people walking over black ice past the city's schizophrenic architecture.

Here there were no Hansa palaces, just granite Soviet headaches and smoky 19th century dwellings and tacky postmodern office buildings lined up alongside one another. Ladas and BMWs rolled by. It was interesting, but not pretty. It was getting hard to see Tallinn by now anyway. Even though it was only 3.30 pm, it was almost dark.

At the bus station, I climbed aboard the Viljandi-bound bus with Epp and looked down on its passengers, many of whom looked back at me with steel-blue eyes and expressions of almost menacing indifference. What was their problem?

As our vehicle stole away into the somber, snow-covered Estonian countryside, I worried about where I was headed. On one hand, I was happy to be back together with Epp. On the other hand, I had no idea what I should expect from this country.

❀ ❀ ❀

The door creaked open, and a small woman welcomed us in to the evening glow of her apartment. Near my feet, a round, rat-like dog with silvery eyes scurried to sniff my pant legs, as if it knew instinctively that I was not of this land.

"Don't worry about him," the woman said of the dog. "He's 15 years old and almost completely blind."

Our host's name was Helle. She was Epp's father's sister, a school teacher. Even in the dark, I could see that she looked a little like Epp.

Our bus from Tallinn had arrived in Viljandi, the town where Epp was born. From there, we had caught a local bus to Helle's town, Suure-Jaani. The entire trip took half a day, though for me it was actually a continuation of the previous day, when I had flown through the night from New York. In fact, I am not sure what day it was. It just didn't matter anymore.

Both Viljandi and Suure-Jaani were wooden towns with an assortment of older medieval churches and ruined military fortifications. Suure-Jaani was built around the gothic steeple of St. John's Church, in whose graveyard was buried Epp's mother Aime, her father Andres' parents Eerik and Aino, and their parents too. The history of Epp's family seemed to hang in the misty air, and this woman Helle had known all these people. She had also known Epp her entire life. Maybe she even had a hunch of what kind of man I might be, given the circumstances.

Despite all of these ghosts, Helle was jolly. She made us tea and then reclined on a couch watching a music program on TV. A man with flowing hair who looked a bit like a bullfrog was growling in front of a male choir.

Of course, I had no idea what the guy was saying. But Helle was so emotional from watching him sing that she had to rub a tear from her eye.

"That's Tõnis Mägi," she said proudly. "He's Estonia's Mick Jagger."

Estonia had its own Mick Jagger? I was puzzled by the thought. What else did it have that I had never heard about before?

In the other room, Epp went to work loading our bags with books. She had hundreds and hundreds of Estonian books that she had stashed at Helle's place in between her many moves. I glanced at the authors: Milan Kundera, Erica Jong, Ellen Niit, Johannes Semper.

"Where do you get all of these?" I asked.

"Estonians like to collect books," Epp said. "We are going to take as many as we can back to Tallinn."

By 'we,' she obviously meant me, because I was charged with heavy lifting. I decided not to protest. Instead, I walked to the apartment window, and looked out into the black night across the frosty landscape. In the distance, a small playground stood empty. Then I suddenly noticed a photo hung on the wall. It was a sepia-toned photo of a little blonde girl that I instantly recognized – Epp as a toddler.

20-odd years ago, it seemed, she had been sitting here, in this very same room where I now stood, in the center of a pile of old toys with a determined look on her face, bashing the head of a dismembered doll against the floor.

"She has always been this way," I realized, looking at the determined little face in the photo. "And now I am completely at the mercy of this crazy little girl."

CAFÉ
MOSKVA

Café Moskva* stood on Tallinn's centrally located Freedom Square, or Vabaduse Väljak. *I was expecting something a little more Moscow, but this was a modern, Scandinavian-looking establishment, and I felt a little cheated as I walked through its glass doors and tried to find a seat in one of its shiny, metallic chairs.*

I had come to meet Ivan Spengler, the head of the local office of the *Baltic Times*. I had visited their webpage and saw an advertisement for freelance reporters. Enchanted by the opportunity to be some kind of foreign correspondent, I sent every person in the company an e-mail until I heard back from them. Ivan by e-mail agreed to meet me at Café Moskva so we could discuss working together.

But there was a problem. I had no idea what Ivan looked like. I had no idea what he sounded like. I didn't know if he was

---

*　'Moscow' in Estonian.

young or old or fat or thin. All I knew was that his name was Ivan, and I figured he would be easy to find in a café.

I was wrong. Café Moskva was packed with people having lunch, and each time I tried to make eye contact with somebody, to see if they were also looking to meet someone, I would be met with a nasty, menacing look, that same "leave me alone" stare that had greeted me on the bus.

"Excuse me," I asked a blond-haired guy in English. "Are you Ivan?"

He muttered something in Estonian that sounded like the equivalent "fuck off," and turned back to reading a copy of *Õhtuleht*. There was a picture of a burned car on the cover. I had been in Estonia less than one week, and I could tell this tabloid newspaper from the other papers by its covers of car wrecks or half-naked chicks. They published a newspaper everyday of the week, save Sunday, when their stands would say *only one more day until a new Õhtuleht*. Estonia could hardly wait.

So the blonde guy wasn't Ivan, but who was? I decided not to push my luck, and sat down at an antiseptic metal table. Café *Moskva*? Where were the balalaikas? The ballet dancers? The wild Russian girls in go-go boots? This place had all the funk of a glass of milk. Café Moskva? More like Café Oslo.

I looked around again, but decided I didn't want to piss off any more Estonians. So instead I looked at my hands, and I became so absorbed with them, that I barely noticed when an older man with a moustache and leather cap sat down at the same table with me.

"Are you Ivan?" I asked in surprise. I found it hard to believe that this gray-whiskered old man was running the local office of the *Baltic Times*. He must be a hardened old-timer with loads of experience, I thought. Together, we could go far.

I asked him again, "Are you Ivan?"

"Ivan?" he replied, showing a mouth full of enthusiastic yellow teeth. "*Dah*!" Ivan began to speak to me in Russian. "Blah blah blah," he rambled on, "blah blah blah blah blah blah blah."

But Ivan's smile soon turned to a frown. Maybe he became more confused as my eyes grew wider and wider with disbelief. How could this guy run an English-language newspaper, if he didn't even speak English?

"Excuse me," a voice said. "My name is Ivan. I believe you are looking for me." I looked up and saw a young man in his mid-20s staring down at me.

This younger Ivan was dark-haired, of slight build, and seemed reserved with a touch of anxiety. I could tell immediately that he was a journalist. He seemed to be analyzing everyone around him without betraying any emotion.

The young Ivan said a few quick Russian words to the older Ivan, and the older Ivan seemed to apologize, picked up his leather cap, and moved to a nearby table.

"Sorry about that," Ivan said sitting down. "How long have you been in town?"

"Just a few days."

"Then I suppose you have managed to hit the local bars."

"What do you mean?"

"You know, Hell Hunt. Nimeta. Nimega.'"

---

* 'Gentle Wolf, Bar with No Name, Bar with a Name' in Estonian.

"I haven't been to any bars," I felt awkward. "But I have been to Suure-Jaani."

"I see," Ivan frowned. "I am sure you will get to sample our local nightlife soon enough."

Ivan proceeded to tell me about the *Baltic Times*, how much it paid, how many articles I could expect to write per week. He asked if I understood basic finance and governance, to which I always answered in the affirmative, even if I had no idea what he was talking about, such as:

"You know how our local stock market works, don't you?"

"Oh, sure."

"Good. Just wanted to check."

It reminded me of when my brother had gone job hunting in New York. When he was eventually hired, he spent the following week studying books on topics he had claimed he was an expert during the job interview.

Somehow the topic steered from the *Baltic Times* to the Soviet past. Maybe Ivan wanted to impress me. Or maybe he thought it was interesting. Either way, I listened.

"I remember when Brezhnev died," Ivan said. "And then Andropov and then Chernenko. It seemed like every year there was a new face we had to learn."

How was it that someone that was my age could remember these men? Ivan must have only been in kindergarten when this happened. Did kindergartners learn about Brezhnev? I didn't remember learning about Reagan in kindergarten.

"Then I got to watch the Soviets go home," Ivan continued. "Now, that was really interesting."

I tried to imagine how the Soviet collapse must have felt for a Estonian Russian adolescent like Ivan, but the dry tone in which Ivan seemed to paint all of life's big events told me that he had already succumbed to the profession of journalism. Murders, rapes, explosions, natural disasters, assassinations – these were but facts to be represented as accurately and emotionlessly as possible.

One time in journalism school, our instructor had told us how he had seen an entire village destroyed by a mudslide in Mexico. "Ooh, how interesting," a fellow student had cooed. And she had meant it because, to her and aspiring reporters like her, an encounter with misery was a great way to win a Pulitzer Prize.

According to Ivan, the 2003 parliamentary elections were coming up and this would provide us with a host of story ideas. At one end of the street where Epp and I lived stood a tall poster of a portly middle-aged man named Edgar Savisaar who was thrusting his arm up in the air displaying a victory sign with his fingers. Above the local Internet Cafe, there was a gigantic billboard of Juhan Parts , the leader of a new political party called "Res Publica." The sign read *Vali kord!* or "Choose order," as Epp had translated it one day. I quizzed Ivan about the different parties.

"So, I take it that the *Isamaa** party is conservative," I said.

"They are right wing," Ivan confirmed.

"And *Reform*?" I asked.

"They are also right wing," he said.

---

*   'Fatherland' in Estonian; the party is known internationally as 'Pro Patria'.

"What about *Res Publica*, what are they?"

"Well, they are a new party, so no one knows for sure what they stand for. But, they are basically right wing," he said.

"What about this Savisaar guy?" I said. "I kind of like him, he reminds me of Nixon."

Ivan put his coffee down. "Savisaar?" he said, coughing in disbelief. "You like him?"

"Well, he seems like he has a sense of humor," I said, "as opposed to Juhan "Choose order" Parts. What are Savisaar's politics like?"

"He's from the Centre Party, which supposedly represents the center," Ivan rolled his eyes, "but, basically, he just represents himself."

"Are there any other parties running?" I asked.

"Well, there are the Moderates."

"I take it that they are moderate."

"Exactly."

"So you have three right-wing parties, two centrist parties, and no left-wing parties in Estonia," I said, scratching my head.

"They are pretty hard to tell apart," admitted Ivan, "but I can always tell where the politicians are."

"How's that?" I asked.

"Be on the lookout for a lot of shiny, black, expensive cars."

For the first time, Ivan smiled. It seemed that he would let me write some articles for his newspaper.

CHOOSE ORDER!

Unlike most Estonians, I was late – as usual. My first week teaching at a local language institute had ended up with me nearly getting dismissed.

I was strolling back to the institute after sneaking a healthy lunch of ginger chicken soup at a café when I got the call from the institute director.

"Where are you?" she said urgently. "Your student is here!" he's waiting.

"Don't worry, I am on my way," I was calm. "I'll be there in five minutes."

"FIVE MINUTES!" she barked. "You better get here in two minutes. He's paying for this!"

"We'll just tack on the extra time at the end," I tried to smooth things out.

"But maybe he has another appointment after ours," the director snapped. Then she hung up.

Ouch. Why were these Estonians so uptight?

I quickened my step and apologized to the director as I entered the institute though my inner hatred of these punctual Estonians grew by the second, until I met my student.

His name was Anatoli, and he was a Ukrainian. Middle aged, he wore, like almost all other men, a leather cap and a moustache. I decided to find out what was the difference between Russians and Ukrainians. "When Russians want to thank someone they say *spasibo*," he explained. "Ukrainians say *diakuju*."

We didn't get much farther than that. Anatoli told me that he spoke English fluently and, since he rarely spoke, it was hard to tell.

The language institute director told me after the lesson that there were two types of students: those who thought they already knew everything and those who were too shy to even try speaking. Anatoli, she said, was of the first category.

I also pressed her about getting some kind of paper that would show I was employed at the institute. With this paper, I could file for a living permit so I could stay in Estonia beyond the allowed 90 days.

"Yes, yes," she waved to me as she fished a few kroons out of a metal box to pay me for the lesson. "We will work something out for you. Don't worry about it."

❀ ❀ ❀

Though the institute director was less agitated about my lateness, it was a problem that didn't seem to go away. I complained to Epp about these Estonian "Time Nazis," but she explained that Estonian time allowed no substitutes; 10 am was

10 am, not 10.06 am. That was six minutes late. "Late" seemed to be a dirty word; if a person was "late," they were irresponsible. One could simply not be "good" and be "late." These were mutually exclusive words. So any Tallinner could see me hurrying across the icy streets to my appointments, checking my watch to make sure I was on time. "Oh no," I looked at my watch one morning, "I'm going to be late!" I came down hard on my ass, followed by my back. The hard Tallinn ice offered no support. It only gave out pain.

"Oh Christ," I sighed as I pulled myself off the ground a few seconds later. I rubbed my rear. "That's going to leave one hell of a bruise."

My mission was to meet three Estonian TV journalists to figure out what it was they needed to learn. After surfing the ice for a few more minutes, I walked into the large, gray, Soviet-style building; this was the house where the state-owned channel *Eesti Televisioon* was made. My students were already waiting for me.

There were three of them: Anu, Marko, and Kadri. Epp told me that they were pretty famous, but none of them looked familiar to me as we had no TV in our apartment.

Each of the TV reporting trio was different in his or her own way. Anu reminded me of Pippi Longstocking with her wide friendly smile and red hair. Marko was more reserved. He had short blond hair, was meticulously groomed, and wore a smart sweater vest. Kadri was the most introverted. She had darker hair and was dressed in gray. All of them were perfectly dressed with perfect skin, perfect hair, and perfect teeth. I was impressed.

"*Tere, mina olen Justin*,*" I said to the trio as we moved into a conference room. "I am originally from New York, but my girlfriend is from Viljandi County," I explained, in Estonian. The three looked at each other in disbelief.

"How long have you been here?" asked Anu.

"Just a week and a half," I answered.

"And you speak Estonian already?" Marko wrinkled his forehead.

"You know," Anu said, "there are some people who have been living here for 50 years who can't even say that much." Marko nodded. Kadri said nothing.

I thanked Anu for the compliment. It was so easy to make these Estonians your friends. All you had to do was memorize a few of their sentences.

The first part of our lesson focused on getting Anu, Marko, and Kadri to correctly phrase some questions. After a few cups of coffee, though, I decided we should talk about current events to exercise their language abilities.

"So what do you think about the elections?" I asked Anu. "Who are you going to vote for?"

"Well," she said, running her fingers through her perfect red hair. "I have always liked *Isamaa*. They seem so nice because they want to protect our language and our culture. I really believe in protecting our traditions and our songs."

Marko shook his head. "I don't think we have to go crazy about protecting our culture that much," he said, "Estonians take themselves too seriously."

---

*   'Hello, I'm Justin' in Estonian.

"But you are an Estonian, aren't you?" I said to Marko.

"Yes, I am. But I used to be a Soviet citizen too," he was ironic. "In fact," he continued, "I used to be in the Soviet army."

I looked at Marko and imagined him standing at Checkpoint Charlie in Berlin, holding a machine gun in front of his perfectly coiffed hair and sweater vest.

"You used to be in the Soviet army?"

"Sure," he was nonchalant. "I served for two years."

And to think, all those nights Americans had gone to bed fearing nuclear holocaust, they had been quivering in fear of Marko, the skinny, stylishly dressed Estonian TV journalist.

"But, like I said," he continued. "It's not that I am not Estonian or that Estonians do not exist as a country. But we shouldn't take ourselves so seriously. I mean, it's not like we are *French* or something!" I wasn't sure if Marko held the French in high regard, or thought they were a little too pompous about their identity.

"Well, anyway," interrupted Anu. "I have decided it here. I am supporting *Isamaa* this time. Maybe."

"But what about this "*Vali Kord*" guy – Parts?" I asked.

"Choose order?" said Anu. "That sounds kind of scary."

"And you, Kadri?" I asked our group's most reserved member.

"Who? Me?" she answered, looking up from her coffee.

"Yes, what do you think about the elections?" I said.

"I have no opinion," she said. "I'm just a journalist."

❋　❋　❋

Like a beginner ice skater, I made my way across the treacherous sidewalks of Tallinn to the office of the *Baltic Times* on Pärnu Road. It was in a building that Ivan had told me was once the main headquarters of all Soviet newspapers in Estonia. In the office, I was met by a blond-haired secretary named Heli.

"You must be Justin," she welcomed me in. Outside it snowed again. I could see the sheets of white coming down in the gray light. The phone rang. "Just a second."

Heli spoke in English to the person on the phone. Then she hung up and dialed another number, this time speaking in Russian. Finally, she ended that call and said something to Ivan across the room in Estonian. He replied tersely and went back to clicking on his computer.

"Well, come on, sit down, here, here is a copy of this week's newspaper," Heli said. She thrust a fresh issue of the *Baltic Times* in my hand.

It felt like a high school newspaper and looked like one, too. And yet, the news on the cover was all international news. My stories were in here too. Maybe they would take me somewhere.

I thumbed through the paper and waited for Ivan to finish a phone call. The air was dry and smelled of coffee. The phones and computers were old but functional. This was the world of Ivan and Heli. They were here five days a week and had been here together in this office for years.

"I'll need a copy of your passport and some additional information so that we can pay you." Heli thumbed through some books and let out a sigh. I could tell the weather was getting to her too.

According to the newspaper, a group of young Russian nationalists called "*Shtab*" were trying to lead a popular uprising against school reform in Latvia. The Estonians, meantime, still were waiting to sign a border treaty with Russia. Christ, these Russians were crazy. Did they ever relax?

"What's going on in our world?" I said to Ivan after he hung up the phone, holding up the paper.

"Russia accuses the Baltics of discrimination," he yawned. "Estonia still doesn't have a border agreement. This stuff never really ends."

"Why doesn't Estonia have a border agreement with Russia?" I was slightly worried. "I mean, there is a border, right?"

"Of course, there is a border, but Russia is a huge country," Ivan was impatient. "They probably still don't have agreements with a lot of countries on their border."

I wondered if, at somepoint, Russia planned to extend its border zone to the Baltic Sea. It was as my friend's father used to say: *The Russians cannot be trusted.*

"I don't get the sense that Estonia and Russia are the best of friends," I said.

"Well," Ivan sighed, "there's always the minority issue here."

"This I know," I said. Every guidebook informed you that a quarter of the Estonian population was ethnically Russian. It hadn't always been that way – most had come in the 1950s or 1960s. While Americans were eating TV dinners and buying Elvis Presley records, Estonia was undergoing a huge demographic shift.

The prewar Estonian population, I later learned, was 88 percent ethnically Estonian. By 1959, though, it was 74 percent, and by 1989, it was just 61 percent. In 2003, the ethnic majority comprised 68 percent of the population. The Soviet population transfer pressure cooker had been turned off, but one could see why Estonians had been alarmed by this. I decided it was a peculiar legacy, but I was glad Estonia hadn't turned into Chechnya or Yugoslavia.

"Well," I told Ivan, "what can you do." I had no answer for such a complex situation.

After typing a bit more, Ivan continued the discussion. "A lot of people still don't have citizenship. That's a thorny issue, too."

"No citizenship? How is that possible?" I was surprised.

"Well, they restored the state in 1991, so all those people who moved here after 1940 had to apply for citizenship in the restored state," Ivan.

"1940? That's a long time ago."

"But that marks the start of the occupation," Ivan said. "According to their logic, anyone who entered afterwards did so illegally."

"But if it's such a problem with Moscow, then why don't Estonians just give them citizenship then?" I said. "I mean, what's the difference? They live in Estonia now."

"Because that's not what the right-wing parties are about," Ivan shrugged. "You could say that it's against their principles."

"So how can people without citizenship get it?"

"You have to take a test in Estonian language and culture."

"So why don't the people without passports just learn Estonian language and culture and get citizenship?" I said. "It can't be so hard."

"A lot of Estonian Russians are their own worst enemy," Ivan admitted. "Some of them would rather complain than do anything about their situation."

"But you can get by in Estonian."

"Oh yeah, you and I can learn a language. That's true. But for old ladies in Narva? For them, it's impossible."

"How so?"

"After the war, the Soviets only settled Russians there," Ivan was incredulous, as if I was the most naïve American writer who dropped by to freelance yet. "It's a completely Russian-speaking place."

"So, it's like the Estonian Vyborg?" I had heard several times during our summer trip of how the Soviets had taken Finland's blessed town Viipuri. Olesia, the Russian correspondent, had asked Finnish Foreign Minister Erkki Tuomioja about it during a press conference. Erkki was bashful and said that Finland had no claims to anything on the Russian side of the border.

"Sort of," said Ivan, "except that Narva isn't part of Russia."

"But does your father speak Estonian?" I asked.

"Oh, my father speaks perfect Estonian," Ivan was proud. "So does my wife."

I looked at the golden wedding band on his finger. I hadn't noticed before that young Ivan was married. He was only 23 years old. People got married young in Estonia.

"But how did you learn Estonian?" I asked.

"I studied journalism in Tartu University," Ivan said. "But, yeah, it took me a long time to learn. I'd be surprised if you ever become fluent. You have to remember that this is a very difficult language. It is not Spanish."

Little did he know that Spanish was also a tricky language. I had studied five years of it in high school and college and could only remember a few phrases. Ivan's take on the situation of Narva grannies seemed to make sense.

This Estonian minority politics 101 lesson was interesting, but I wasn't sure of what questions were appropriate to ask my Russian-speaking friend. Russians seemed so sensitive. Who wanted to make them angry?

"Well, do you personally feel discriminated against?" I ventured.

Ivan sunk back in his chair and stared at his computer. He looked really annoyed.

"I think that this subject has been written about to death," he turned to me. "It has been exaggerated and blown out of all proportion. But I would be lying to you, if I said that discrimination does not exist in Estonia."

"If it makes you feel any better, discrimination exists in America, too," I said.

"I have heard something about this," Ivan smiled, happy to change the subject.

"Here," he said, rolling in his chair over to a large bookcase. "You should read these. They'll help you better understand this crazy country." He held out a copy of *Baltic Revolution* by Anatol Lieven and *Return to Independence* by Rein Taagepera. I took them from him and put them in my bag.

"By the way," Ivan said. "In your last article, you said Estonia 'gained' independence in 1991. In the *Baltic Times*, we say it 'regained' its independence."

"I'll remember that," I said, before turning to go. "Thanks for the books."

BUCKWHEAT PORRIDGE IS GOOD FOR YOU

When most people think about adjusting to life in a northern country during the winter, they think about being depressed by the dark and the cold and turning to alcohol for relief. But it wasn't the weather that starved me of joy in Estonia; it was the awful food.

Each day at our Kentmanni street apartment progressed with depressing helpings of *pelmeenid*, root vegetables, and the Estonian delicacy, *verivorst* – blood sausage. *Pelmeenid* were boiled meat dumplings served with sour cream. I tried to convince Epp to bake them, but she refused.

"You are like my friend Airi, she likes them baked," Epp said. Airi had traveled with Epp in India. They were close friends. "But *pelmeenid* are best when boiled," Epp assured me. I privately thought of inviting Airi to dinner. Then we could outvote Epp when it came to *pelmeenid*.

When eaten, each dumpling would pop in my mouth, the salty liquid surrounding the boiled pork squirting in my cheek.

They weren't my favorite – ok, they were kind of gross – but *pelmeenid* sure beat blood sausage.

Blood sausage? At first I wasn't even sure what this mellow-tasting brownish substance was, least of all that the reason it was brown was because it had been made from the blood of once-living creatures. And this was the Estonian national dish? These people were vampires.

"Blood sausage is good for you," Epp said. "It's a good source of iron." When she wasn't eating blood sausage, Epp would also chew on *hematogeen*, which were sort of like blood candy bars. I decided I would love Epp unconditionally, though, no matter how much blood she ate.

Epp would fry up the blood sausage in our barely functional kitchen, douse it with lingonberry jam or sour cream (an ingredient that seemed to be served with almost every Estonian dish) and it was time to dig in.

Each morning, as the coffee brewed and I heard my overactive partner hustle from one end of the apartment to the other, I would be served a heaping bowl of *tatrahelbed* – a salty, slightly bitter, dark-looking porridge made of buckwheat flakes.

Epp would dump a mountain of it on my plate. I could usually eat about half, if I pretended it was something else, but the other half would not budge.

"Why don't you eat your porridge?" Epp asked one morning.

"It's salty."

"But that's how it's supposed to be," she said, with the finesse of a culinary expert. "In Estonia, we eat this kind of porridge with salt and butter. It's good for you. One plate full and you won't have to eat until dinner."

I could not stomach the idea of one more spoonful of salty porridge.

" In America, we eat our porridge sweet, with jams or raisins or maple syrup," I said in response. I felt like a snob for turning down her salty porridge, but was it so wrong to have some control over what I ate?

"*Syrup*?" she said, turning up her nose at the suggestion. "That's gross."

"Well, this porridge tastes like the Atlantic Ocean. You might as well feed me a bucket of seaweed."

"I cannot cook us a sweet porridge," Epp shook her head. "What would I eat then? You said you were willing to adapt."

She had me there. But then I had an idea.

"How about we do it this way – you just make the plain porridge, and I will put sugar in mine and you put salt in yours?"

Epp thought about the offer for awhile, then agreed. "Well, if that's the only way you eat your porridge, then that's how we'll have to do it."

❀   ❀   ❀

There was regular food available in Estonia. At the gigantic shopping center down the street, you could find whatever you needed. The only problem was that the mozzarella imported from Italy was several times more expensive than the local brands. So, we did our shopping at the corner shop and at the central market instead.

If our apartment had stunk of the Soviet 70s, then the central market was like a step into a fantasy or science fiction film, a place where you could watch a butcher carry the leftover parts of a pig from the trunk of his Lada. Old drunks, their faces swollen and hands cut, staggered along the market pathways. In strong tones, young Russian-speaking children begged their mothers for bags of candies. Feral dogs chased each other as old ladies used iron scales to measure out kilos of potatoes and carrots and mushrooms and cucumbers.

Epp said she loved the colors of the marketplace, "It reminds me a bit of Asia, and it is cheaper here," she said. After each visit we would trek back to our apartment with backpacks full of grapes and grapefruits. But we always returned. Fruit didn't last long in our house.

Epp may have loved the central market with all of her bohemian heart, but the movement and the smells and the noise and the negotiating just made me queasy. I wanted to load up the bags and go, but Epp enjoyed haggling with the sellers who were always trying to add in a bonus cauliflower or watermelon or a jar of honey for just a few extra Estonian kroons.

And of course, they sold plenty of blood sausage and buckwheat flakes at the central market. How could they not sell these necessities at Epp's favorite marketplace?

"Why are you buying more buckwheat?" I said one frosty Saturday in frustration.

"Because I really, really like the taste of it," Epp said, loading four bags into my already heavy backpack. "And besides, it is very healthy. It has a lot of minerals."

"Listen, I can't eat any more porridge or grapefruits or blood sausage," I said again. "I need something more substantial."

"But you have lost weight," Epp said. "You are in better shape than you were in Finland, that's for sure."

I couldn't argue with that. Pants that had once barely fit now slid over my hips. Who knew how much weight I had lost from walking everywhere and subsisting on porridge and boiled meat dumplings?

"Look, I am going to buy some chicken schnitzels," I said, finally. "I am hungry. I need to eat something I like for a change."

"That's fine," Epp agreed. "We should buy more different things! I am going to buy some fish."

"Be my guest."

We walked into a cold, stinky room filled with cuts of fish. Epp decided to buy a medium-sized smoked fish, which they handed to her in a plastic bag.

"Aren't they going to cut the tail off it?" I asked.

"Why would they?"

"Do you plan on eating the tail?"

"Maybe."

"Ok, but, whatever you do, don't offer me the tail."

"Oh, don't worry," Epp licked her lips. "This fish belongs to me."

Epp ate the smoked fish that night while holding it by its brown pointy tail, like it was a chicken bone. After the fish had sat in our fridge for just a few hours everything, including the milk, tasted like a stagnant pond. I could see its carcass at the bottom of the fridge, its little tail poking out of the old plastic bag, as if to say hi.

"It is like living with an Eskimo," I said.

"Yeah, I am just like a little Inuit girl, aren't I?" Epp taunted me.

"You smell like one."

"But you still love me, right?" she smiled at me, holding the fish.

I smiled back. In fact, I even kissed her, fish breath and all.

❈ ❈ ❈

One difference between the central market and the big supermarkets, other than price, Epp explained, was clientele. The central market's shoppers were often Estonian Russians. These were people who I imagined lived in a different, Russophone world where color and vibrancy and noise and open-air markets were cherished and the ice cold sterile Scandinavian supermarkets were always second best.

Russians were like Jevgeni from our trip, I decided. They liked to drink and swim nude across lakes and learn new dirty English words. They liked to haggle over carrots and hang out with feral dogs. They were a bit wild, but they enjoyed life.

At the basement Internet Cafe in the city center I would frequent, the majority of customers were definitely of this flamboyant Slavic variety. Loud disco music pumped from the speakers while adolescent body odor choked the air.

Whenever I would leave the underground lair of the Estonian Russian Internet Cafe, I would sigh in relief to be back in the comforting silence of Tallinn in winter. I wanted to like these people, but Russian life seemed exhausting.

Because a sizeable chunk of Estonian Russians lived in Tallinn, it also meant that there was a linguistic divide. Many of them spoke neither Estonian nor English, leaving me to try and communicate using sign language.

Epp had grown up in the Soviet era and had lived in Tallinn for a few years. She could speak Russian if needed. But I barely knew any words.

One day outside our Kentmanni apartment, an old man in a leather cap approached me and started talking. He was crooked and walked with a cane. The old man had a thick white moustache, and eyes that burned with dissatisfaction.

If he had spoken Estonian, I would have been able to tell him I had no idea what he was talking about. I could tell him that I was from America, and that I only spoke a little Estonian. But he spoke Russian, so all I could do is stare back at him like a mute.

"Blah blah blah, blah blah blah blah blah?" he asked.

I didn't respond.

"Blah blah! Blah blah blah?" His voice grew more agitated.

"I cannot understand. I am an American," I said in Estonian. Maybe he could understand? He did live in Tallinn, the capital of Estonia. Unfortunately, it seemed as if my Estonian only made him angrier.

"Blah blah!" he yelled. "Blah blah blah!" The old man gestured violently with his cane.

"*Nuuzhna nozh**!" I erupted, summoning my tough inner Slav. "*Zatknis***!"

The old man suddenly looked frightened. Then he limped away.

I felt embarrassed for both of us.

---

*   'I need a knife!' in Russian.
**   'Shut up' in Russian.

VODKA
SOCKS

The cold, dark night assaulted me from every direction
as I walked home to Kentmanni Street. It had started
to snow again, and it seemed as if every joint in my
body ached, most of all my lower back.

I had been trying to soothe the pain from the cold by taking hot
baths at night and maybe sneaking a hot bath in the middle of the
day, too. As I would dip into the bathtub, I might spy a black and
blue mark on my leg or behind from another mishap on the ice.
In this cold air though, my gloves felt as if they didn't exist. The
wind blew snow down my neck. And I could not even remember
when I last saw the sun. Estonia was testing my fortitude.

From the sidewalk, I could see Epp through a lit window. She
was making a pizza. No more blood sausage or milk soup! I felt
victorious. I turned up the steps and entered our apartment.

"So, how was your day?" asked Epp, as I undid my frozen
boot laces in our apartment.

"Good." I still felt too cold to talk.

"Did you meet up with Anu, Marko, and Kadri again?"

"Yes."

"And how did it go?"

"Ok," I grunted. "How come they always look so good? I mean, larger than life."

"What do you mean?"

"They are always just so well dressed. And they have perfect skin."

"Ha!" Epp snorted. "That's because they have TV make up on. I am sure they don't look so great when they get up in the morning."

"Did you know that Marko used to be in the Soviet army?"

"That's how it worked," Epp nodded. "They drafted everyone. Estonians would be sent to places like Uzbekistan and the Uzbeks would be sent here."

"Really?"

"Several of my friends were in the army, too," she said. "They all say it was awful: you had to speak Russian so much that you would start thinking in Russian. You almost forgot Estonian."

She set out two plates of warm pizza on a bamboo mat on the floor – we had no room for the table in our kitchen, Epp said, because "this house was built at a time when the Soviets thought that nobody would need kitchens and would eat in canteens together."

"They really thought that people would eat potatoes together and talk about class struggle?"

"It didn't work," she shrugged.

I changed the topic. "I spoke with Ivan again about the restoration of the Estonian state."

"I remember when they registered everybody in early 90s," Epp said. "We had to find the documents of our grandparents showing that they were born in the Estonian Republic. It was kind of cool. And we were lucky: my grandparents had their documents plus they were born in the right timeframe, during the Estonian time."

"We also talked about statelessness. And about the language exam people have to take."

Epp took a bite of her pizza and poured a cup of milk from a plastic bag. Here in Estonia, I noticed, milk came in bags. My favorite was the red one with the fluffy white clouds. Even if Estonians could be icy in person, they sure knew how to make everything cute and childlike, even their milk.

"I don't think it is asking so much for the people who moved to Estonia to take a test," she said, "but I don't think these old ladies in Narva should have to take one."

"Well, the state could have deported them, like they did with the Germans in Kaliningrad," I said, eating my pizza. I tried to imagine Ivan and his wife arguing with armed guards in their perfect Estonian while being loaded into a train to be sent "back" to Russia. It seemed preposterous.

"No," Epp said. "I also think it is wrong that people call them colonists or that people dislike them for it," she said. "You have to look at it from their side, too."

"Well, what do they think about it?"

"My childhood friend's parents came here from Ukraine," said Epp. "They had no idea that Estonia was an occupied little country – to them it was all the same. Factories in Estonia needed workers, so they just put up advertisements in Russia or in Ukraine, and people decided to come here. They had no idea it was any different."

The whole package of historical restoration, citizenship, and Soviet migration policies seemed surreal. Here we were in 2003, and yet the past was always lingering just behind us. When would the past catch up to the present? When would there be no stateless people, a border treaty, and a harmonious world where old guys on the street understood you when you answered them in Estonian?

"Listen," said Epp, "I made an appointment to go visit Salme this weekend." Salme was Epp's great aunt, Epp had spent many nights at her place during her interludes of homelessness.

"You know," said Epp, chewing her pizza, "Salme was deported."

"She was?"

"Salme was really young. She was only in her 20s. And she wasn't very healthy; she barely made it to Siberia alive."

"But why did they send her to Siberia?"

"Because Martin, her father and my great-grandfather, owned a farm. They were *kulak*s. Rich peasants." What was it about Soviet words that made you just want to puke all over the place? Bolshevik? *Kulak*˙? *Kolkhoz*˙˙? They all sounded like intestinal disorders. I'm sorry to tell you this, sir, but you have an advanced case of *kolkhoz*.

I felt my stomach twist again. I set my fork down on the mat and put my face in my hands.

˙   Literally 'tight fisted' in Russian – a name given to the independent farmers that were the target of Stalinist repressions.
˙˙   'Collective farm' in Russian.

"You don't look so good," Epp said. "Maybe you should go lie down." I pulled my clothes from my aching body and tucked myself into our fold-out bed. Outside, I could see sheets of snow covering the sidewalks in front of the dimly lit American Embassy. I held my cold hands over my noisy belly and tried to get some rest.

Hours later, I felt like a ship adrift in a thunderstorm. First it came in, quiet but ominous, and then my insides began to rock. I tried to steady my boat, but I could not stop the shifting feeling beneath me. The room began to turn. Then the dreams began.

They shot at me, like lightning bursts, one by one.

We were back on the ferry from Helsinki to Tallinn, the first time I came to Estonia.

"So what's your father's name?" I asked her.

"Andres."

"Andres Väljaots?"

"No, Andres Saluveer."

"But how come you have different last names?"

"Because I am divorced."

"Oh."

"How do you feel about that?"

"Well, you're not the first divorced woman I've met."

Like so many dreams, these faded into one another, the scenes suddenly changed. One moment I was on that ferry, then suddenly...

I was watching TV with my family. They seemed anxious about the big things happening in my life. I told them not to worry.

"It will only be for five months," I told them. "I am not going stay in Estonia forever."

I felt as if they didn't believe me. How come they didn't believe me?

"This will be really good experience for me. I can be a foreign correspondent. That's what I want to do."

I writhed in bed, molested by the images. I tried to think of something peaceful, something that would help calm the earthquake that was going on in my stomach.

I saw palm trees and taxis and then I saw Epp. She was walking down a busy street in a city. There were lights and movement everywhere. People on motorcycles and street vendors selling barbecued duck. She sat down to take a bite of some dinner.

Except, I had never been there in Malaysia, had I? Wait a minute? Faces seemed to swirl around my head.

I shot up out of bed and made for the toilet at the end of the hallway.

"I don't feel so good," I gasped, before my mouth opened and an ugly explosion of partially digested pizza hit the inside of the toilet bowl. I gagged three or four more painful times until my stomach was empty. With the last gag, a tiny pea from the pizza I ate hours before hit the toilet bowl and rolled on to a stack of magazines beside the bowl.

I noticed then that one of the magazine covers featured a woman who looked exactly like Kadri from the English lesson. But what was Kadri doing on the cover of a magazine? It just couldn't be.

"I'm never eating peas again," I coughed, before heaving one more time. I could now feel Epp's hand on my head.

"Get a cold towel," I demanded

"What? What for?"

"Get a towel and wet it with cold water, that's what I use to stop," I heaved again into the toilet, "to stop puking." My stomach twisted in pain. The tiny WC stunk of my sickness.

Epp brought me a wet towel and I put in on my neck to stop the heaving. Slowly my inner pain resided and I caught my breath.

"I think the peas made me sick."

"I think you have a virus."

"I feel a bit better now," I croaked. I stumbled back down the corridor, rinsed my mouth out in the bathroom sink, and moved uneasily towards the bed.

"Help me take your socks off," Epp said.

"Huh?"

"You have a high fever," she said. "I am giving you vodka socks."

"Vodka what?" I asked.

"Vodka socks."

"No, you're not!"

"Just relax." I could hear her in the kitchen opening our refrigerator, and then the clink of what must have been our bottle of vodka, the one that Epp had bought one day – "Just in case."

Epp came back in the room and helped to pull the wet socks over my cold feet. It felt uncomfortably damp at first, but then the alcohol began to react with my skin. My feet started to tingle, then burn. Suddenly, they were on fire with warmth. While I enjoyed the comfort of alcohol on my ankle joints, Epp went back into the kitchen.

"I know you can't eat this right now, but just smell it."

"What is that?"

She held out a tin of chopped garlic in her hands and set it beside my head. "It helps to cure any disease."

"Garlic helps to cure any disease?" I mumbled. "Cool."

Epp nestled beside me in our bed. I fell back into a deep sleep, the garlic fumes filling my nostrils, the fiery socks of vodka burning my feet.

I did not dream.

AUNT
SALME

Every morning started the same.

Epp would rise in the dark and boil the water for coffee. Then
the radio would click on and the announcer would begin wish-
ing little old ladies all over Estonia "Happy birthday."

There was Maali in Rapla who was 80, or Helgi in Rakvere
who was 75. And, did you know, that Laine and Endel from
Põlva have been married for 50 years? Then the announcer
would play old-fashioned music that would curl and drift into
the morning blackness.

Each day was dark as the Arctic. When would the sun return? Who knew? It had been days since I last saw it, and even
then it was more of a haze than real sunlight. It was now Feb-
ruary. There was nothing to look forward to but more blackness for weeks to come. I felt an itch to drink alcohol, and I
hadn't even had breakfast yet.

The tinny radio that sat on the fridge began to beep. Then
the news announcer came on. Estonian sounded like one long

mumble, except every day I was able to detect more words from the mumbling. Today I heard something about a ship and Sweden and the sea: those were the only words I understood.

"Did something happen to a ship in Sweden?" I asked Epp.

She came in with two coffees and set one down beside me. The announcer's monotone voice settled into the distance. "A small ship sank; everyone is ok. Nobody died," Epp said.

Epp had told me during my first day in Tallinn about the *Estonia* ferry disaster in September 1994 when 852 people went down with the *Estonia*, which was en route from Tallinn to Stockholm.

Epp's uncle Tiit was a musician who played on ferries and Epp was at Tiit and his wife Reeli's apartment that morning. Epp said the phone line was clogged by Tiit's friends who were calling to make sure he wasn't aboard the *Estonia*.

I had yet to meet Tiit and Reeli, but I knew what they looked like. In our cabinet there was a stack of photo albums of Epp's life from which I could learn all about her family and her past. My favorites were the black and white ones with her experimental late 1980s haircuts.

"We tried to copy that one from a magazine," she said, gesturing at a really strange haircut that might have suited Duran Duran or A Flock of Seagulls.

"A friend told us that you would get a cool 'disco' haircut if you tie a tight and high ponytail and then cut it off. We tried it, but it didn't work out so well." In her past, Epp had worn a huge compass on her wrist and had a pet rat. She had a poster in her room of a Swedish hair metal band called Charizma. Epp even sang for me their song:

Estonia and Sweden, join hands, join hands together, we are friends forever.

I wondered what it would be like if in 1990 someone had introduced me to this crazy 16 year old from the Soviet Union with the monosyllabic name, experimental haircut, and little pet rat, and told me that she would one day be the love of my life.

In 1990, I was in the fifth grade. Kids my age were more concerned with Vanilla Ice than *perestroika*. And only the coolest, most suave fifth graders had girlfriends. I wasn't one of them.

❋ ❋ ❋

Aunt Salme lived in an apartment building in an area of Tallinn called Õismäe. Epp showed it to me on a map.

"I can't believe they built a huge apartment complex in the shape of an eye," I said.

"It's not an eye. It's supposed to be a flower. *Õis* means blossom."

"It looks like an eye to me."

We dressed as warmly as we could and ambled like penguins over the icy sidewalks towards the Estonia Theater in downtown Tallinn to catch our trolley to the eye of Õismäe. We had to be there at 11 am. Salme was expecting us.

It was a milky winter day. The trolley passengers were glum. The interior stunk of slush and sweat. Outside, the gorgeous city I saw in August streaked by in lifeless shades of brown and gray.

We passed a place advertised as *Rocca al Mare*. It was a nice, Mediterranean name: I imagined there would be groves of lemon trees in *Rocca al Mare*, and sturdy Italian fathers with donkey-drawn carts making their way down to buy fish at the harbor. As we looked over the flat, gray bay through the steamy trolley window, though, I could see *Rocca al Mare* was undeserving of its name.

From the fog, Õismäe emerged. Towering apartment blocks, each one like the other, loomed out of the mist like enormous cargo ships. These were the gray, fossilized dinosaur droppings of the Soviet state, each one an identical copy of the other.

"It looks like a gigantic mental institution," I told Epp, as I looked up at the honeycomb apartment buildings. Epp said that she had a problem. She couldn't remember where in this maze of humanity Salme lived. Only Epp could be on time and forget where she was going.

"I think she lives in building number 66, but I am not sure," she said. She looked worried. It was now 10.56 am. We were almost late. No Estonian was allowed to be late, even when visiting an elderly relative.

"Do you really think Salme has other plans on a Sunday morning?" I tried to calm her. "She will be there even when we are a little late."

"That's not the point," said Epp. "It's rude not to be on time. She is waiting."

Epp and I arrived at building number 66, but then she realized she had another problem. "I think she's in apartment number 78, but I am not sure," she fretted. Epp buzzed number

78, waiting for a response. It came. "*Du!*" a man said. That was definitely not Aunt Salme.

"Maybe it's building 67?" she said. We ran to the building and Epp buzzed number 78. This time, no voice answered but the door to the building opened. We took a chance and went inside. The lift in the building was barely big enough for two people. I wondered what might happen should it break down while we rode it up to the seventh floor.

We got out and walked to apartment number 78, but something was wrong.

"This just isn't it," Epp frowned. "It doesn't look like this." She glanced at the concrete stairs and we went up. "Ah, that's right," said Epp. "Salme's apartment is number 87, not number 78." She knocked at the door and we stepped back.

A second later, a little old lady with spectacles and curly gray hair was staring up at us with steely blue grey eyes. It was Salme. I looked at my mobile phone. It was exactly 11.00 am.

"You are on time!" Salme said joyously. "Come in, come in – the tea is ready!" She hugged Epp then turned and hustled back in the apartment. I could see the steam from the tea pot blowing in the little kitchen.

"How is it possible that the tea is already ready?" I asked Epp. "We just got here."

"Because that's how Salme is," she said. "She probably started boiling the water at 10.50 because she knew we'd be here at 11. And we were actually on time. High five!"

❄ ❄ ❄

On March 24, 1949, Salme awoke at 4 am to the sound of a doorbell. Into the house stepped three men – two Russian soldiers and one plainclothed Estonian. The men checked the passports of those in the house and Salme was told to come.

"Where to?" she asked.

"We don't know," the men responded.

She was driven with other deportees to the train station and loaded into a wagon with 50 people. The wagon was made for transporting animals. There were no toilets.

Salme and the others were given water to drink three days later, on the 27th – two buckets for all 50 people to share. The next day the rations were the same. On April 3rd, two weeks after the start of the trip, they were finally given something to eat. Soup. Salme did not hear about her family for years. Her father had already been deported to the camps, and she had no idea where her sister and mother were. Altogether, 20,000 people had been deported from Estonia during that one day.

Salme almost died on that train to Siberia. She had suffered from a high fever and had a problem with her thyroid, because of the stress. She survived, but one leg never was the same again. Epp told me this story as Salme brought us tea.

I could tell Salme had some kind of walking problem. I saw she had a metal cane in her hallway. But Salme still managed to flit around the apartment, laying out cups of hot tea and biscuits, putting on the TV for us, asking us if everything was alright. She was a good host.

I settled down into the living room, a biscuit in my hand, and looked out the window to the gray fog that blanketed the other apartment buildings. A trolley snaked by a kiosk in the distance. The windows were gray with condensation. A few plants strained their necks to soak any tiny bit of sun out of the harsh Estonian sky. This was Salme's dreary urban world.

Epp switched through the channels on Salme's TV until she came to a talk show hosted by a guy with dark hair who looked like an undertaker.

"That's Aleks Lepajõe," Epp said. In Soviet times, the half-Ukrainian Lepajõe had at some point escaped on a boat to Finland where he became a jewelry thief and was arrested, she said. But Lepajõe was just so charismatic and charming that the female Finnish guards fell in love with him and decided to let him go free and host a talkshow in Estonia. Or something like that.

To my surprise, part of Lepajõe's show was in English. He interviewed an Italian named Giovanni. Epp explained to me that Giovanni was one of the most famous Italians in Estonia because he allegedly set fire to his ex-girlfriend's parents' car in a fit of jealous rage. For this and other reasons, he would probably soon be deported. I immediately took a liking to Giovanni. He, at least, showed some vital signs.

"Who are the other famous Italians in Estonia?" I asked. "Maybe we can become friends with them?"

"The most famous is Ernesto Preatoni," said Epp. "He's a real estate mogul."

I knew it! Even in Estonia there were Italian guys setting fire to cars and engaging in real estate deals. I wondered if every country had its own Giovannis and Ernestos.

Salme finally entered the room and took a seat in the chair facing us.

"It's good to see both of you," Salme settled into her chair. I had begun to understand a lot of what people around me said, but in this situation, Epp translated for me

Salme had a nice demeanor. I didn't want to do or say anything that might offend her. She took a sip of her tea and looked down at a small sheet of paper in her hand.

"Your name is Justin," she said, "and your last name is Preatoni, right?"

"Not Preatoni, Petrone," I said back in clumsy Estonian.

"Oh, I just was planning to ask, if you are a relative of this businessman Preatoni?"

She crossed out a line on her sheet of paper.

"And do you have a job?" she asked.

"Yes, I am working as a..." I struggled to find the right words in Estonian.

"He is working as a journalist and teaching English," Epp assisted.

"Of course, of course," Salme said. She crossed another line off her sheet of paper.

Epp and Salme's voices hovered barely above a whisper and Salme would suck in air and say "*jah*"* or "*vist*"** from time to time. I stood and walked across the room to the book shelf where I looked at pictures of Salme's family, none of whom, it seemed, liked to smile in family photographs.

There was a man and woman in one photo, both with blue eyes and dark hair. They did not smile. They did not frown. They did not look happy or sad. Their faces expressed no emotion.

---

*   'Yes' in Estonian.

**   'Maybe' in Estonian.

In another photo, there was a teenage boy with curly brown hair and a smaller girl with straight hair. The boy hid some mild angst, while the girl betrayed a modicum of hesitation. The emotional temperature in this photo, though, was similarly Antarctic.

"That is my son and his wife," Salme called out. "And those are my grandchildren." I looked at the ice-blooded androids in the photos and at Salme and her list of questions and tried to figure out what kind of developmental accident had caused Epp to turn out so different than all her relatives.

Epp was vibrant. She was alive. Or at least she had been at some point. Because in this setting Epp was no different. She was one of them. Quiet. Dry. On time. What had happened to my globe-hopping Mongolian bohemian Epp? It was as if she had been kidnapped by Estonians.

Looking at Epp and Salme talk even I began to feel anemic. Their world seemed so dry, so placid and lifeless. There were no sudden movements or surprises or gut-splitting jokes. There was only tea and order.

Salme was Epp's mother's aunt and since Epp's mother Aime had died and Aime had no sisters, Salme was one of the closest female relatives Epp had. I tried to imagine Epp as an old lady and looking like Salme, so gray and calm and wise, but I couldn't.

Salme pulled herself from the chair and limped in my direction. She drew a few leather-bound photo albums from the wall and handed them to me to look at while she continued her discussion with Epp.

I began to turn through the old photo albums. Salme was from a village called Varbla in Western Estonia. In the book, there were postcards and photos from the 1920s and 30s. There were images of kids at school, picnics in parks, and sunny days at the beach in old-fashioned bathing suits. There were even some photos where the people were smiling and appeared to be having a good time.

Then there was a photo of a white, tree-less landscape. Then there was another. In a third photo, a ghetto of wooden shanties stood in the foreground, lines of black puffing from their makeshift chimneys.

"Where is this?" I asked Epp.

"Siberia," Salme answered.

I nodded, but I had nothing to say. What do you say to someone who has been deported to Siberia?

"How long were you there?" I asked through Epp.

"About seven years."

"That's terrible."

She said nothing and moved slowly towards the bookcase and pulled a small box from the shelf.

"Look, they gave me this last year," she held out a medal.

"Who gave it to you?"

"Our President Arnold Rüütel. There was a ceremony in honor of us, for the hardships we faced."

I looked at the medal. Go to Siberia in 1949 and get a medal for it in 2002.

"Did your grandma Laine also go to Siberia?" I asked from Epp.

"No, Laine and my mother Anna hid in the forests," said Salme in response. "It was very cold," she said. "They deported us in March."

Salme's mother Anna, then aged 44, and Laine, aged 18, had stayed in the woods until it was clear that the trains to Siberia had left. Anna's husband Martin, a veteran of the Estonian War of Independence, had been deported the year before.

"When my great-grandma heard that the deporters were coming, she grabbed my grandma and they ran to the forests," said Epp. "During the next days, when they were hiding in the bushes they saw village people wearing their clothes. The other Estonians looted the place after they were gone."

It was the last time Anna and Laine Laanemaa would be able to be in the house that Martin had built on land he was granted for his service in the Estonian army. They had lost everything in one night.

"They had to leave their home village and start from scratch in Eastern Estonia," said Epp. "Very secretly."

"Oh."

"This is just one side of my family. My other great-grandfather was deported too."

Salme quietly put her medal back in its place on the shelf and walked over to turn off the end of Lepajõe's show.

Epp had told me the whole story, but Salme hardly said a word. I wondered if she had ever spoken with anybody about her trauma. Did they have therapists for deported people in Estonia?

Salme was a woman who had been deported to Siberia and nearly died there. She must have something to say about it. If I had been deported, I told myself, I would be consumed by vengeful anger. Somebody would have pay for it. I would be like Giovanni, lighting cars on fire.

But Salme said nothing. She just stood there for a moment as if lost in a shadow of the past, then turned to Epp and me, smiled politely, and asked if we would like to have more tea.

PHOTO GALLERY

The crazy Estonian girl and me in Venice. We were traveling in different countries. During the journey, I learned to trust the water and myself, and I learned about Estonia through her stories.

Young foreign correspondents in Finland. This shot was taken after another awkward sauna experience, where we were expected to disrobe, squeeze into a dark hot room, and whip each other with birch branches.

The Finnish Foreign Correspondents' Program had one mission: to attract young journalists to Finland and brainwash them about how great Finland is. Years later, I believe its effects are irreversible.

Finland was my last hope. It was calling me in my sleep from Helsinki, an open-air mental institution on the other side of the world.

This is my first photo of Tallinn, taken on the day that changed my life.

Living across the street from the US Embassy was never boring. There were always interesting individuals standing in the street in line to get a visa, and on some other days we could see rallies, some more peaceful and some more aggressive.

This photo was taken next to our window – such scenes were common due to US government decisions in 2003.

When I first heard the name "Stalin's house," I suspected the basement to be filled with unmarked graves and torture devices. In reality, it housed a fascist casino and bourgeois nationalist interior design shop.

The local news said that these birds forgot to fly south for the winter and it was the responsibility of humans to keep the birds alive. Like many Tallinners, we started to feed the birds on a regular basis.

"The clerk pulled out three bags of what appeared to be dried moss with some twigs and leaves mixed in. This couldn't be the medicine Epp had requested. I felt like we were doing a drug deal. Did she grow this stuff at home?"

"Here in Estonia, I noticed, milk came in bags. My favorite was the red one with the fluffy white clouds. Even if Estonians could be icy in person, they sure knew how to make everything cute and childlike, even their milk."

Here is a store named 'Store.' In Estonia, they have flower shops named 'Flowers,' donut shops called 'Donut Shop,' and book stores called 'Books.' When it came to store names, Estonians hid their creativity.

"Epp ate the fish that night while holding it by its brown pointy tail, like it was a chicken bone. After sitting in our fridge for just a few hours everything, including the milk, tasted like a stagnant pond."

One Estonian pastime is to go sledding on hills like these, which they proudly call "mountains." In this photo, we are in the so-called 'Estonian Switzerland,' in Karksi-Nuia.

Epp, me, and the church where she was baptized when she was 16. Why so old? Many young people were attracted to religion when the USSR crumbled. "It was a year when many people found God," Epp said.

"I know a German guy who thought that building was marked 'Zero A',"
Epp said of the Oa Street sign. "He couldn't believe that we start buildings
with the number zero in Estonia."

Supilinn, a district in Tartu, is an odd combination of perfectly renovated
doll houses and abandoned buildings that have either burnt recently or will
probably burn tomorrow, unless somebody decides to renovate them.

In Estonia, almost every family has someone whose year of death ends with a question mark.

The air in Tartu is a little different than Tallinn's, even if it is hard to describe. Maybe this is the infamous 'Spirit of Tartu'?

Epp's grandpa's expansive book collection was typically Estonian. Do they really read the collected works of Balzac? Grandpa said that he has read the works of Estonian national writer Anton Hansen Tammsaare, but not every volume of Balzac.

I found myself in big trouble once, trying to talk a little girl out of collecting every stick she found on the street. Later I learned that many Estonians (those who have wood furnaces, at least) have the same hobby.

Many Estonians do not use electric dryers. They still use old-fashioned clotheslines.

"I looked up into the trees and breathed in the cool air coming off the lake. This looked like a good place to spend eternity."

Making bread with Amanda, the host of a tourism farm in South Estonia. Behind them is the sauna — the centerpiece of every proper Estonian homestead.

"Forty years from now, we could settle our own farm somewhere in South Estonia and come to love the smell of hot manure and freshly-baked bread."

Here's the bread that Epp and Amanda made at the tourism farm. Estonians have different names for breads depending on colors and consistency. White breads are called *sai*. Black breads are called *leib*. This variety of beige-colored bread is called *sepik*.

Whenever I see dried fish, I lose my appetite!

Over one year, so much happened in this tiny land that it stopped being foreign. Estonia and I became intimately acquainted. In the end, I came to love it, for both its beauty and its ugliness.

OLD
FRIENDS

---

*I was seated at a café when I saw him. He was wearing
a leather jacket and purple cowboy boots.*

A fashionable scarf was slung over his shoulders and expensive sunglasses framed his face. Even in trendy Tallinn, he stuck out. It was Don Priit Kõrvits of London who had returned from his passport forgery business for a quick trip home to Estonia.

"*Tere-tere**," I said to Priit, rising to shake his hand.

"Yes, hello," he said back in English, shaking mine and sitting down. Epp was at the bar ordering us coffees.

"So how are you?"

"Fantastic." His eyes were hidden by shades.

"And how are the guys in London?"

He frowned. "Not so good."

"What do you mean?"

---
*   'Hello-hello' in Estonian.

"Two weeks after you two left, they raided the hotel where Valdek was working. So he was expelled."

"Where is he now?"

"In Tallinn. I just saw him yesterday."

"That sucks."

"They also picked up Piret and Liis, two of the girls who were living in the apartment," Priit said. "Pigs." He sat back in his chair, arms folded in disgust.

Epp joined us from the bar with a few coffees in her hand.

"What's wrong?"

"Priit lost half his roommates," I said. "They got deported."

"That's terrible."

"Can you go back to the apartment?" I asked Priit.

"Oh, sure," he replied. "I have all the necessary documents, so I am not worried about myself."

I wondered if his necessary documents were fake or real, but I did not ask. Instead, I changed the subject. "But why are you in Estonia?"

"I am looking for a job," he smiled. "I want to get out of the UK. It's a stupid bloody country. All of Tallinn," he gestured angrily at the café walls with his fists, "could fit in a single neighborhood of London, and nobody would notice! And yet they deport us."

"So what kind of job are you looking for?" asked Epp.

"That's what I wanted to talk to you about. Did you say you have contacts in the TV business?"

Epp and Priit switched to Estonian and talked for 20 minutes, sucking in air while they chatted, pausing occassionally to spit a few times in the air. Meantime, I scribbled in my journal and watched the people drift in and out of the café.

One of them I recognized. It was Steve from the *Baltic Times*. Or *Reuters*. He wrote for all the publications he could. I had met Steve at the Baltic Times office one day. He had swooped in, out of breathe, quickly uploaded some photos of Stalinist wall paintings to Ivan's PC from his memory stick, introduced himself to me as Steve from San Francisco, and left us – Ivan, Heli, and myself – all within the space of 10 minutes.

He instantly became my ex-pat hero. Steve said he had been living in Estonia for over 5 years. Before that, he had lived in Moscow, where he had moved right out of college in 1991, right after the August coup. He said he moved to Estonia because the "changes here occurred faster than in Russia."

Steve spoke Russian fluently and I imagined that he knew how to do things, things I couldn't do. Perhaps he knew how to find an electrician or a plumber. Maybe he knew where a person could send a fax. Why, I bet Steve even knew how to get an Internet connection installed in his apartment.

"What's up, Steve?" I called from across the café.

Steve eyed me from across the room. He stood there for a second, and then let out a cautious "Hi" and moved his hand up and down in a clumsy wave. In spite of all of his worldy experience, he seemed as if he was afraid of something. I got up and walked towards him. As I made my way through the cafe, my foot hooked a chair and I stumbled to the ground.

"Are you ok?" Steve asked, as I pulled myself up.

"Yeah, I'm fine." I dusted my pants off.

"So how have you been?" he asked.

"Good. I've just been finishing up a story about the Tartu Airport for the newspaper."

"Tartu Airport? Yeah, I think I wrote a story about that a year ago. I guess it's still not ready for commercial traffic? And Tartu remains as an isolated city in the middle of boggy South Estonia?"

"No, there is no commercial traffic yet."

"Yeah, I didn't think so. I saw you work in the office. I never work in the office." Steve shook his head in disapproval.

"Why not?"

"Oh," he looked away. "Because."

Did I fart or something? Why was Steve acting so strange? Or was he just always like this? Well, San Franciscans are known for their idiosyncrasies, I told myself.

"I have to work in the office," I explained. "We don't have Internet in our apartment."

"Why don't you have Internet in your apartment?"

"My girlfriend's office is right down the street."

Steve froze. "Who's your girlfriend?"

"She's sitting over there."

Steve looked pale. "You mean the one in the red jacket?" he whispered.

I turned and saw cute blond dressed in red sipping her coffee and thumbing through a newspaper.

"No, not her, over there." I gestured towards Epp.

"Oh, next to the guy in the shades," Steve smiled and relaxed his shoulders. "Well, I'm just glad it wasn't Pille."

"Who's Pille? The lady in red?"

The crimson lady took a bite of a pastry and turned the page of her newspaper. She pushed a lock of golden hair from her face, and looked quickly in our direction, but pretended not to notice us.

Steve nodded "She's my ex-girlfriend. We don't talk."

"I understand."

"Tallinn is just not big enough for all my ex-girlfriends," Steve shook his head. "Oh, look at the time!" he shot a look at his watch, and then cast an eye back towards Pille. "I've got to get going."

"Where are you going?"

"To Paldiski. It's a town northwest of Tallinn, he said. "I have to write another travel piece."

"Paldiski? I don't remember reading about it in the guide-book. Sounds like a cool place."

"Oh, it's a blast," Steve said. "Paldiski used to be pretty big military installation, home to 15,000 people. Now there are only 4,000 left. There is only one restaurant there. I just can't wait to go. Maybe I'll see you around at, uh, the office."

Steve then turned and fled from the cafe. I walked back to Epp and Priit. But Priit was too busy to notice me. He was talking on his sleek new mobile phone.

"Yes? Yes? Yes. I'll be there in five minutes."

Priit put his phone back into his leather briefcase and stood up.

"I'm sorry, but I am a very busy man," he was polite. "We'll be in touch."

Priit did get a job in television, co-editing a reality TV show. On the few occasions I saw it, I would make sure to watch his name in the credits. I was happy that he had given up his forgery business in London for something more legitimate in Estonia. He was a talented person. I didn't want to see him waste it on something that not only could get him in trouble, but also make Estonia appear bad to others. It was because of guys like Priit that people like Epp and I had to undergo extra scrutiny at passport control points, was it not?

Unfortunately, Priit's business went wherever he went. One day Epp called me. She sounded upset.

"Janek just called me. Priit was arrested. They raided his apartment while he and his girlfriend were at home," Epp said.

"Shit."

"There were passports all over the table, and he had one open on his computer."

"And where is Priit now?"

"He's in jail."

ATHENS ON
THE EMAJÕGI

---

*Epp had decided to pursue a master's degree in
journalism and she often spent nights poring over texts
of unreadable theoretical nonsense, asking me to define
words I had never even heard of. Each weekend she
would travel by bus to Tartu so that she could attend
class. This time I decided to join her.*

Tartu, population 100,000, is Estonia's second largest city. Bisected by the Emajõgi, Estonia's largest river, Tartu is home to the country's most prestigious university, founded by Swedish King Gustav Adolph in 1632, plus countless other institutes and societies. For these and other reasons, Tartu is called "Athens on the Emajõgi," though no doubt with a strong hint of Estonian sarcasm.

The only problem was getting there. We had no car, and the rail connection ran at inconvenient times, so, unless we were willing to hitchhike the 185 km through the countryside to Athens on Emajõgi, we were taking the bus with everyone else.

Award-winning scientists, prominent journalists, Rasta-farian backpackers – they all took the bus to Tartu. There was no air connection, and who wanted to shell out the money for a private car or struggle to catch the train from Tallinn's seedy train terminal?

Some of my first articles in the *Baltic Times* dealt with these transportation issues. Why was there no air connection to Estonia's second biggest city? Why did the Tartu train station still look like a condemned building that was liable to cave in? Who could help turn this creaking, post-Soviet country into a modern Nordic one with train connections and regular flights? If one wanted to get from Helsinki to Turku, he or she had a whole day full of fast train connections from which to choose. But getting from Tallinn to Tartu? Get on the bus.

It took almost three hours for us to drive the 185 kilometers to Tartu by bus. During the trip, I became consumed by the nothingness of the Estonian countryside. There were thick forests and white fields and lakes and nothing else. I started to understand why a country bigger than Denmark could be home to nearly one-fifth as many people.

"Where are the towns?" I asked Epp. "Where are the people?"

She was reading one of her unbearably boring school texts. I was about halfway through *Baltic Revolution*.

"We just passed through a town," she answered.

"Where? I didn't see one."

"We were just in Anna, a town, or a village at least."

"That wasn't a town back there. That was a church and a gas station."

"That's how towns are in Estonia," Epp said. "An Estonian's dream is that he can just see the smoke from his neighbor's chimney."

I settled back into Anatol Lieven's *magnum opus* about the recovery of Baltic independence. First published in 1993, then updated in 1994, *Baltic Revolution* was still considered 10 years later to be the best source of information about the Baltic countries. The names inside were all familiar: Mart Laar, Marju Lauristin, Edgar Savisaar – each one of these faces might be in tomorrow's newspaper in 2003. It was if time had stood still.

There was one problem. The UK-born author Anatol Lieven at times struck me as smug. He described Estonians as "irritating" people, as if he wasn't aware that British people were among the most difficult people in the world.

"Why don't you like British people?" Epp asked.

"Because they tried to burn down the White House during the War of 1812," I replied. "And because they can be irritating."

"What about the Beatles?" she asked.

"What about those drunken football fans in track suits that always bug me in airports. It's a nation that exports difficulty."

After more endless stretches of forests and fields, some dotted by small country houses displaying the blue, black, and white flag of Estonia, we entered the city of Tartu. There were no big buildings at first, just wooden houses. Here was Estonia's second largest metropolis – a collection of 19th century homes with gingerbread latticework.

As the road sloped down into downtown Tartu, with its larger, prettier buildings, Epp bounced in her seat, pointing out different houses to me.

"That's where I sent my brother Aap to school; and down there, that's where the biggest national daily *Postimees* is, and that's where I lived once, and my other old apartment used to be over there."

This voyage to Tartu was like a trip into Epp's past. This is where she had gone to university. I wanted to know more.

"How many places did you live in Tartu?"

"That's a tricky question, let's see." Epp counted silently to herself and kept track of her thoughts on her fingers. Epp wasn't very good at math, though, so she had to start over a few times.

"Can I borrow your notebook?" she asked. I gave it to her. For awhile she scribbled. Then she stopped.

"Seven different places!" she exclaimed. "No, wait a minute." She looked at the journal. "Eight. Eight different places!"

"How did you wind up living in eight different places?"

"It just happened."

"I want to know."

"Well, I first came to Tartu to go to university and I went to stay in a place owned by my grandfather's friend, a 70-year-old guy. But I didn't realize that he was also living in the house. He wasn't there all the time, he had another place, too, but he came and went whenever he wanted..."

"And he started to hit on you?"

"No. But he did smell really bad. And he was a ratpack."

"You mean a packrat."

Epp nodded. "I cleaned up the kitchen one day, and threw away some old newspapers and he got really mad. So then I answered an ad in a newspaper for another apartment. But," she looked away, "do you really want me to continue with this?"

"Should I be afraid?"

"I happened to get involved in some kind of family drama. The landlady was an old lady who rented me a whole two-bedroom apartment."

"And she started to hit on you?"

"No, but her son was some 40-year-old weirdo, and also had the keys and he came one day and was yelling that his mom had no right to rent this place out. And he refused to leave, then his mom came and they were yelling at each other."

"I didn't think Estonians were capable of yelling at each other."

"They were Russians," she said, "and they were pretty loud. So I stayed in that place for maybe two weeks, but the guy was living in the other bedroom and was waiting for me to leave."

"And then what happened?"

"I found a pretty good two-bedroom apartment after that and for many months it seemed alright. Then one morning the husband of my landlady showed up. First he wanted to borrow money, but then he came back two hours later, kind of drunk, and started to hit on me."

"I knew it!"

"I had to throw him out from the apartment. And then he lied to his wife that I was hitting on him – and I had to leave."

I rubbed my face with my hands as Epp recounted her soap opera of a life before meeting me. And to think, we were just in the Tartu period of her life; we hadn't even gotten to India yet.

❋ ❋ ❋

"Come on," Epp said as the bus pulled into the station, "This way."

I was nervous about meeting Epp's sister Eva. I knew the kind of pull a woman's sister could have on her and I was afraid that if Eva didn't like me it would be the end of me and Epp.

Sisterhood, I hypothesized, was its own secret institution. I had watched my mother and her sister countless times dissect our family life. Nobody wanted to mess with a pair of Italian sisters. But Estonian sisters? I was about to find out.

Eva's house was in the old town of Tartu, across from St. John's Church. I arched my neck back to take in the Gothic steeple. Epp told me that there had also been another big church in Tartu, St. Mary's, that was even more gigantic, but it was destroyed in the Great Northern War between Sweden and Russia. The University building stood on St. Mary's ruins.

While St. John's was functional, parts of it were still derelict. It looked as if it had survived something awful. According to the sign outside, that something awful was the Second World War. Germans and Russians had battled on either side of the river, blowing Tartu to pieces. Wherever you saw a park or a new building in Tartu, it is likely an ancient one had stood there before the war.

And that's how things were in this country. No matter where you went in Estonia, every building, every person had a sad story to tell. Whether it was deportation or war or famine, even the most magnificent churches could not escape Estonia's less fortunate fate.

"I think it's so cool that Simona lives across from this church," said Epp. "She keeps saying that when they finish renovating it, she would like to be baptized there."

"She's not baptized?"

"Eva and Pets aren't religious," Epp said. "I think they think my interest in religion is a bit weird."

I suddenly spied a shadowy figure in the distance. Outside the wooden gate across from the church stood a tall sillouctte and when we got closer I recognized the woman's face in the shadows from Epp's photo albums. It was Eva, Epp's only sister.

Eva was only a year and a half younger than Epp, making them something like twins. Epp could not remember a time when she didn't have a sister. Eva was always there. She was part of Epp's reality, as much as her father was and mother had been.

But these sisters were different. Epp was short while Eva was tall. Epp was a journalist while Eva was a confectioner. Epp had been to China, India, Malaysia, Tunisia, and, just recently, New York. Eva had been to Finland and Latvia.

"I asked my sister why she doesn't want to travel," Epp had told me once, "and she said that because she doesn't need to, because all places are the same. Can you believe that?"

I didn't know what to tell Epp. I thought of Eva taking her young daughter Simona to Israel or Cyprus or China in a backpack, camping out in the mountains as Epp might have suggested. I dared not tell Epp that Eva was right. Even if I had not met Epp's closer family yet, I had understood one thing: Epp was the crazy one. And I had to agree with them. How could Epp really think that her sister would give it all up to go to an ashram in India?

"*Noh, tsau**!" said Eva. It had been awhile since she had last seen her only sister, and their personal contacts had been intermittent over the past few years, with all of Epp's traveling taking her outside of Estonia. Despite all this time apart, Epp did not hug her sister. They did not kiss, or even look especially happy to see one another. Instead, they stood apart in the cold air, maintaining a safe distance. I was confused. In my family, if you saw a relative, even one you had never before met, you made sure to give them an obligatory peck on the cheek.

Epp introduced us and I looked in Eva's light blue eyes, illuminated by the snow and a nearby street lamp. Her face reminded me of Epp's, but I didn't detect anything unusual as she looked at me. I extended my hand, and Eva gave it a strange look, as if it might have something in it. Then she realized I was greeting her, and briskly shook it.

Any anxiety I might have had about meeting her began to fade as Eva turned to open the gate. Eva, as far as I could tell, was a normal person and had no desire to sabotage my love life. Maybe she didn't care. Maybe Eva got up each day and put her pants or skirt on and went to work and didn't worry about her sister's choice in men.

Eva guided us past the gate into a frozen cobblestone courtyard. These cobblestones had probably been here since before the town where I grew up in New York had been settled by English colonists in the 17th century. I was impressed. What a cool place to live. Americans shelled out serious money just to spend weeks in Europe's old cities. Eva and her family lived in one.

---

*   'Well, hi!' in Estonian.

"She says that it used to be Peter the Great's stable," Epp translated.

I was happy to know that I would be spending the night in the same place where Peter the Great, Russia's cartoon-like leader, waxed his moustache and saddled up his steeds. I was happy to know that only horses had lived here in the past. Maybe nobody had been deported from here or executed in the cellar. On this night, we would sleep among the ghosts of long-lost imperial horses.

Eva turned the key to her apartment, and we walked through a dark, smoky corridor that gave way to the thick warm glow of Eva's apartment. As we stepped into the light, a light gust of movement bounded from behind the kitchen door.

"Rawrrrrrr!" A small shape cried and jumped out from behind the door to greet us. At first I didn't recognize this frightening little elf, but then saw that it had two small blue eyes and a tuft of platinum hair pulled up into a ponytail. It was Simona, Eva's five-year-old daughter.

Epp crouched down and bore Simona up in her arms. "*Tsau*, Simona," she said, kissing her cheek. At least they kiss children in this country, I thought, even if they don't kiss adults.

Simona giggled and growled again and struggled with Epp, who placed her back on the dark, wooden floor. Simona sprinted off into another part of the apartment. I undid my boots, pulled off my jacket and gloves and scarf and sweater in the black warmth of the hallway, and stepped into a dimly lit main room that was even warmer.

Eva's apartment looked as if it had been lived in for decades. It wasn't dirty, it was just worn. The furniture was old and the floors were cracked and creaking. The carpets and drapes were clean but looked ancient. The toilet also inspired nostalgia, but in a different way. As I sat on it later, I came face to face with an old poster of New Kids on the Block on the toilet wall. Hadn't anyone told them in Estonia that NKOTB had broken up?

In the main room, light flickered from a TV set. Eva's partner and Simona's father, Peeter, known to the world as "Pets" sat illuminated.

Pets wore a t-shirt and sweatpants and it looked as if he hadn't shaved for a week or two. He stretched and yawned like an over-fed lion, smiled, and welcomed us into his lair.

"It's about to start," he said.

"What's starting?" I asked.

"Eurovision," Epp responded.

"What's Eurovision?"

"You mean you've never heard of Eurovision?" Epp said while Eva and Pets looked at me in disbelief.

European countries had been submitting songs to the Eurovision song contest every year since 1956, according to Epp, though there were no Estonian or Hungarian entries that year. In 2001, a song called "Everybody" sung by Tanel Padar and an Aruban-Estonian named Dave Benton had carried this little country to victory, as Epp, Eva and Pets all proudly informed me.

"You guys seem like you take this pretty seriously," I told Epp.

"When we hosted the contest in 2002 it was like an appetizer for joining the EU," she said. "It made Estonia appear less suspicious to Europe. All they had ever heard of is was that we were formerly Soviet. But this proved that Estonia was a real country capable of organizing an international event."

Epp had been there, too. She had been in the media tent with the legions of Estonia-struck foreign journalists.

"One Spanish journalist told me that his mother was afraid that Estonia was in some kind of war zone," Epp said. "He said he was shocked by how normal we were."

My attention turned to the noisy TV. Two people that looked alarmingly like Marko and Anu from my English lesson were discussing the Estonian entries.

"Epp, look, it's Marko from my English lesson."

"Of course it is," she said. "He hosts Eurovision every year."

I struggled to understand how a person I had given an English lesson to was also one of Estonia's most well-known TV hosts, but Epp assured me it was quite normal, because "Estonia is so small."

Eva brought in two enormous desserts and laid them on the table. One was a gigantic gooey slab of cheese cake that looked as if it would feed one of Peter the Great's horses. The other was a sugary strudel, as thick around as my forearm.

"Where did you get those?" I asked, trying to be a good guest.

"I made these," Eva said. I realized that, by this point, everything around me had been said in Estonian, and that somehow I had understood most of what they had said. Pets and Eva had ignored my foreignness altogether. This made me feel good, as if they were accepting me as part of their family.

Eva pushed a hunk of strudel in my direction. Epp picked up a spoon and began to shovel cheese cake in her mouth.

"Simona, come quick," Eva said. "Vanilla Ninja is going to be on."

Little blonde Simona hopped into the room wearing a bunny mask. She stood mesmerized as Vanilla Ninja took the stage. The electronic Asian-sounding synths quickly gave way to chunky guitar chords as the group of blonde teenage girls chopped their way through the verses.

Hey, you, welcome to the party / Me and girls feeling kind of naughty / Dealing with hardcore fighting / Hangin' at the club Kung-Fu.

"Shouldn't it be 'Me and the girls are feeling kind of naughty?'" I asked Epp. "Or, actually, 'The girls and I are feeling kind of naughty'"?

Epp looked at me like I was an idiot and took another bite of her cake. "Justin, this is Eurovision. Do you really think the Greeks can tell the difference?"

Simona liked the music. She tore the bunny mask from her face and jumped in front of the TV, making kung fu kicks with her legs and chopping through the air along with the Vanilla Ninja girls on TV. When the song was over, she rolled onto her back, sweaty and out of breath.

Eva brought her a piece of cake.

"I don't want it!" Simona protested.

Eva paid her no mind. "Here, Simona," She pushed the cake in her face, "eat it."

The next song was by a group called Claire's Birthday, it was called "Eighties Coming Back." For some reason, the Estonian Eurovision entries were mostly in English, as if their thought-provoking lyrics about kung fu would inspire votes of approval from Portuguese pensioners and German teenagers.

As the piano rolled into the classy, retro pop, a young man in front of a rock band grabbed the mic and began to sing.

You said let's do it / Let's take it out and dance all night /
But those deep synthesizer sounds freak you out / Whoah...

"That guy sounds just like Billy Joel," I said to Epp, "except better."

Epp moved closer to me and put her head on my shoulder. By the fourth or fifth time Claire's Birthday's lead singer had sung the chorus, her eyes were watery.

"I can't help it," she whispered. "It's just makes me feel," she wiped away a tear, "so nostalgic."

Can you feel it? / It's the eighties coming back / Yeah, I know
it's just the eighties coming / Eighties coming, eighties coming?
Eighties coming back...

"It's just a song." I tried to comfort her, but Epp started to cry.

"It reminds me of the Baltic Chain," she sobbed. "How we stood hand in hand and formed the chain from Tallinn to Riga to Vilnius in 1989. I hope this song wins."

"Simona wants Vanilla Ninja to win, but I think this song will actually make Estonia look good," Pets said. "Justin has heard the joke about Estonians and the elephant, right?"

"What joke?"

"There are a German, a Frenchman, an Estonian, and an elephant," Epp began. The German looks at *zie* elephant and *vunders* how many bones are in its body and how its muscles *vurk*," she said, adopting an accent. "But the Frenchman, he wants to know how he can, how do you say, make a tasty sauce that would best suit the taste of sautéed elephant meat, yes, yes? At the same time, the Estonian looks at the elephant and says nothing. Then he sighs and says sadly: 'I wonder what this elephant thinks about me?'"

"That's the joke?"

"It's supposed to illustrate Estonian self-consciousness."

"Oh," I shrugged. "Ha ha."

Epp gave me a dirty look and elbowed me in the ribs.

Eva handed Pets another piece of cake. I was stuffed from the strudel, but Eva cut me off another slice and refilled my plate. I tiredly pushed a piece of frosty strudel towards my mouth. I didn't want Eva to think I didn't like her cooking.

"Eat, eat!" Eva commanded. I guess if we didn't eat the cake, she would have to eat it. And she didn't want to eat it, she said, because then she would get fat. So we would have to get fat instead.

Simona meantime approached me and pushed a small picture book in my face. I opened it.

"Karumõmm!" she said, pointing at one animal, apparently a bear.

"*Karumömm,*" I repeated.

"*Karumõmm!*"

"*Karumümm.*"

"*Ka-ru-mõ-õm.*"

"*Karu,*" I concentrated, "*mumm?*"

Simona pushed the book away and threw her hands on her small hips, screaming at me in frustration. "She says that you have to learn Estonian," Epp translated.

"Tell her I am from Saaremaa island and I can say only 'ö'," I replied,

"*Ei**!" said Simona, sticking out her tongue. I suspected for a moment that Epp might have been like this as a child.

I tried to resume man talk with Pets. "So are you going to Andres' 50th birthday party next week?" I asked.

Andres was the father of Epp, Eva, Priit, and Aap, he lived in South Estonia, close to the Latvian border in a little village called Karksi. From what Epp had told me, the past decade had been especially hard on him. Never mind the devaluation of the ruble, the adoption of the kroon, and the sinking of the Soviet economy. Andres had real problems. First the house he had built burned down. Then his wife, Aime, had died of cancer. It was hard to tell how he felt about this from the photos. He looked as frosty as Salme's relatives. Still, I was impressed that these hard turns of events hadn't driven him to the bottle or something darker.

"Of course we are going to his birthday," said Pets. "We are taking the bus to Viljandi and then down to Karksi."

"What is he like?" I asked.

"He is a good man," he said. "But he doesn't talk much."

In the past few years, Andres remarried to a woman named Tiiu and some peace had returned to his life. I hadn't met him, but I could sense the relief in the family. There was now some stability. The implosion of Epp's family had ended, and the mending had begun.

"More cake?" Eva interrupted. I looked at the three-quarters of cheese cake on the table and cut off a final sliver.

---

*   'No!' in Estonian.

It may have been a polar night in the streets of Tartu, but in Eva and Pets' apartment it was Africa hot. They had wood furnace heating, and when Eva opened the front of it I could see the hellish fire within. It was hard to imagine how much trust they put in that old furnace, but it kept them warm and hadn't killed them yet. I had seen some old wooden houses blackened by fire in Tallinn though. I spit over my shoulder three times at the thought.

"So, what are you doing for work?" I asked Pets.

"I am waiting for a phonecall," he replied.

"From whom?"

"From a friend of a friend who said he could find me space on a fishing boat."

"And that's all you do?"

"Mmhmm."

"All day?"

"Until I get that call, I am right here in front of this TV." Pets stretched out his arms and yawned. It looked as if he had been sitting there for awhile. The impression of his butt was moulded into the old chair.

"Why doesn't your friend's friend just send you an e-mail?"

"Because my friend's friend doesn't have e-mail," Pets scratched his stubbled chin. "He just calls whenever he is ready to call."

Pets' work situation was interesting, but I decided not to push him for further details. Instead I let him eat cake and wait for the judgment of the international jury on which song would represent Estonia in the Eurovision Song Festival in year 2003.

"It's not fair!" cried Simona. "It should have been Vanilla Ninja!"

Claire's Birthday, with the young lead singer who was better than Billy Joel, had won the night with their nostalgic, tear-inducing song and rolling piano licks. The Ninjas may have picked up new underage fans, but they would not be going to the main event in Riga.

"I'm really glad they won," Epp said. "This is definitely the best song, and maybe we can get some votes from the UK and Ireland – where they actually understand what the songs are about."

The singer, a modest fellow named Vaiko with a cherubic face and scruffy brown hair, thanked the audience. A young blonde woman with a baby then came on stage with him. I figured it must be his older sister or maybe a younger aunt. The singer, though, kissed them both, as if he were the father of the baby. But this young rock star Vaiko couldn't be a father. I mean, he looked as if he was only 18 years old.

"He's married," said Eva. "I read about them in a magazine."

"But how old is he?" I asked, surprised.

"I think he is 21 or 22," she said.

"22? And he already has a wife and a kid? Shouldn't he be in college or something?"

Eva gave me an odd look. I then realized that she must have been around the same age when she had Simona.

"Estonia is different from New York," Epp said. "Here, having a kid when you are young is completely normal."

151

HAPPY
BIRTHDAY
TO YOU

---

*The bus left us in the middle of nowhere in
a snowstorm.*

We – Pets, Eva, Simona, Epp, and I – were in the southern of
Viljandi County, in a village called Karksi. At least the iced over
sign said so. As I could tell, though, there was no village. There
was only a bus stop and a blizzard.

"Where is it?" I yelled into the wind.

"It's down there!" Epp tossed a frosted arm towards a tiny
speck of light in the distance, set beside a band of dark northern pine trees.

The wind blew ice and snow in our faces. I periodically
checked my nose to make sure it was still there. Pets hoisted
Simona on his shoulders, and the four of us began to make our
way through the knee-deep snow towards the distant light.

Except we soon saw that there were two lights. This second
light grew stronger as me moved towards Andres' house.

"What is it?" yelled Epp to Eva through the wind.

Eva looked at Pets who said he didn't know.

As we approached the stronger light, a boxy shape emerged through the black blizzard in the middle of the road. It was a car with its lights on. Someone abandoned his car in the storm and left the lights to warn off others.

"Are you sure this is the right way?" I yelled. Nobody responded. We soldiered on.

Finally, the smaller speck of light began to grow in the black and violent sheets of white snow. It grew into a small box and then I saw a window. Some 15 minutes after leaving the bus behind on the main road, we had made it to Andres' house, the family seat of this branch of the Saluveer family.

I didn't know why, but I was as anxious about meeting Andres as I had about Eva. But this was different. A woman's father and brothers might have ways of settling things should the relationship take a turn for the worse. With men, there is always the threat of physical retribution, I thought. I hoped to make a good first impression.

As I knocked my boots against the wooden steps to get off the snow, Pets opened the main door and we began to file inside.

The house was just as warm as Eva's had been. Beside the tall furnace, its sunset-orange flames open for all to see, stood Andres and Aap, Epp's youngest brother. I recognized them from the photos. Our eyes met.

"*Tere**", said Andres, flashing a damp smile. Aap said "*tere*", too, but neither showed any emotion. It must be really cold down here in Karksi, I thought.

---

*   'Hello' in Estonian.

I extended my hand to Andres' and shook it strongly, the way men are supposed to shake hands.

"Pleased to meet you," I said in Estonian.

"Mmmmmm," he replied.

Epp meantime did nothing. She didn't even hug her father, who she hadn't seen in months. And he made no effort to hug her either. How peculiar.

Yes, there was something very Asian about the whole ceremony. I felt almost as if I should bow or present my business card.

I stood there searching for some emotional energy to ease my way into this new environment. Some smile or nod that would make me feel welcome or even unwelcome. Anything. What did Andres and Aap think of me? As far as I could tell, they had no thoughts. Maybe this was normal here. The Saluveers were just a normal Estonian family who lacked facial expressions. Except, I noticed one Saluveer was missing.

"Where is Priit?" asked Epp about her other brother. Priit shared my birthday and was famous in the family for getting into trouble. I deduced that somewhere in the family tree there was a crazy streak. Epp and Priit had gotten it, but everyone else had been left untouched.

Andres shrugged and frowned. He opened his mouth, as if he might say something important, but then closed it quickly.

We followed Andres into the big hot kitchen. His wife Tiiu was bent over a table, peeling potatoes. She wore an apron and was keeping track of several steaming pots and a roast in the oven. Andres picked up a potato, too, and started to peel it.

"Andres!" Tiiu scolded him. Andres reached to dump the potato in the pot with the others, but Tiiu quickly fished it out and showed him he had missed one tiny black spot.

"Mmmmmmm?" Andres grumbled, slightly disturbed. He stood there for a moment, and then acknowledged that he had no place in the kitchen and settled down to console himself with a birthday bottle of beer.

Tiiu displayed the faultily peeled potato to Elo, who chuckled. "You can't boil potatoes like that," said Tiiu, quickly cutting the black spot away.

Andres smiled bashfully, looked for a moment as if he wanted to say something again, but changed his mind. I searched my mind for something to say to him, but then also decided to say nothing. And, I have to say, I felt better sitting there in silence. There might be something to being Estonian afterall.

After awhile, Epp and I went and relaxed in the other room looking at old photo albums. From what I could tell, Epp had had a glorious 1980s childhood, full of laughter and happiness, much like mine, a childhood of gangs of wild children watched from afar by adults preoccupied with their own personal lives, free to discover the world as they pleased.

After 1990 or so the photos started to look bleaker. Brother Aap was just a baby then, and as far as I could tell, he had been stoic since birth. Where were the photos of a little fat baby Aap smiling and giggling and gurgling? Photos like photos of me and my brother? They just weren't there. This family simply did not smile in the 1990s.

You could watch the hard times descend on the Saluveer family as the mother, Aime, once a beautiful woman, was cut down slowly and traumatically by brain cancer. Andres' expression in the photos turned from content to worried to distraught to detached from the horrible pain of the world.

"Look at the picture," Epp said, showing me a family photo taken after one of her mother's surgeries, "you can see how stressed we all were."

And then, one day, late in the summer of 1995, Aime died. She was only 41 years old.

"Nobody knows why she got a brain tumor," Epp said. "But there are statistics that show the cancer rate rose a few years after the Chernobyl nuclear disaster. It's likely that she happened to be outside when the bad rain came down."

I saw the photos of the funeral in the photo album, as plainly displayed as photos of kids playing or class pictures. And there was even a photo of Aime in her casket. She looked gray and ravaged by the disease that had taken her life. I held back my own tears. I had never seen a photo of a deceased person in a family photo album like that. And to think, it just sat here on the bookcase, outside Aap's bedroom.

"Why do you have these photos of her in this book like this?" I asked. "Doesn't it make you upset? Don't you want to remember her as she was, before she was sick, before she died?"

"I don't know, it's just a habit to put the photos into albums," Epp said. "Death is a natural part of life. You take photos of newborn babies, don't you? We take photos of people whose lives have ended, too."

In New York, at least in my family, nobody would take a photo of a deceased person like that. It would somehow be seen as disrespectful; a violation of their privacy in death.

In Estonia, though, photography seemed to be part of the grieving process. When you died, they held a party and took your picture. This was just something I would have to get used to. I would have to accept this, I told myself, if I was going to adapt to Estonian life.

❀ ❀ ❀

It was a glorious southern Estonian afternoon. The sun showed through all the windows, and the only evidence of the blizzard was the mountains of snow that covered the ground outside. One by one the Saluveers began to arrive and shuffle through Andres and Tiiu's front door.

First came Helle, Andres' sister, the school teacher from Suure-Jaani, and her daughter Triin, a psychologist in Pärnu; there was also Andres' brother Toomas, who looked like Santa Claus, his wife Merle, and daughter Krista, an architect, all from Viljandi.

Each Saluveer greeted me, their clothes dripping from the melting snow, and seemed, as far as I could tell, normal. Did they love me or were they plotting to kill me? Who would know – I could not read anything from their faces. These Estonians sure would make great poker players.

But Epp's brother Priit still hadn't showed up for his father's birthday party. Epp told me that Priit was just like that. He was a person who would disappear and reappear like a ghost. I waited patiently for him to materialize.

The Saluveers seated themselves around a table and began to help themselves to piles of boiled potatoes and hot sauerkraut with roast pork. Then a smaller plate came my way, covered with something translucent and glistening.

I looked down through the shimmering jelly and saw pieces of shredded flesh. Could it be? Meat and jelly together?

"What is this?" I whispered to Epp.

"It's called *sült*. They take the animal meat and boil it until it congeals," she said. She fished a slice of wobbly *sült* from her plate. "You should try it," Epp said, guiding the slime into her mouth. "It's delicious."

"No, that's ok," I said.

I decided at that moment that I would avoid kissing Epp for the rest of the day. Or at least until she ate something else.

"No, really, you should try it."

Andres shot us an interested look across the table.

When Epp was in China she had eaten fried cockroaches. If given the chance, she would eat chilled monkey brains or snake eyeball soup because she was so cool and so global. But to me, at this point, the *sült* looked like something someone had scraped out of New York City's East River where the city sewage pipes terminate.

"You're really not going to try it?" Epp seemed suprised. "What kind of traveler are you?"

I tried to repress my gag reflex and passed the plate of slime and boiled pig meat on to some other unsuspecting victim. For the rest of dinner, I made sure there was no place left on my plate for a slice of *sült*.

Around me the conversations rolled along in Estonian. Though it seemed a speaker would get excited at times, it was usually hushed, as if they were sharing secrets, at least until they had a few beers in them, at which point they reached what I considered to be a normal conversational tone.

The phone rang and Andres went to the other room to get it.

"Maybe it's Priit? When was the last time anybody saw him?" whispered Helle to Epp.

When Andres returned, he sat back in his chair and shoveled another potato in his mouth. The other Saluveers sat in silence.

"Who was it?" asked Tiiu at last.

"A friend," said Andres. The other Saluveers looked at each other, then resumed their whispered conversations. My head began to swell with the Estonian sounds and words. It really hurt. I even held a cool glass of juice up to my temples for some relief.

When dinner was over, I collected the plates from the table and brought them into the kitchen, where pots and fires still smoked from something Tiiu was cooking.

I thought that maybe Pets or Andres or Aap might pitch in by helping to clean up, but they just sat there sipping their beers or, in Aap's case, milk.

I placed the dishes next to the sink and Tiiu said "*aitäh*",* but made it clear she would need no more help.

"Please, let me get some more plates," I said.

"No, no," she declined, showing me her hand as if she took offense. "I'll take care of everything."

Eva approached me with some cake. I took it and sat down beside Epp on a couch.

---

* 'Thanks' in Estonian.

159

"You know what," Epp said. "In Estonia, men almost never help in the kitchen."

"Why not?"

Epp searched for an answer. "Because it's women's work."

"I didn't really have a strong desire to wash dishes anyway," I said. "I just thought it was polite to help out."

Later, the party guests filed out the door and shook my hand again, one by one. Cousin Triin grabbed my hand and said, in perfect English: "Goodbye, hope to see you again!"

"You speak English?" I was stunned.

"Of course," she said.

"And I do, too," said cousin Krista gripping my hand and smiling.

"You do?"

I realized then that no matter what my language was, the Saluveers weren't going to change their internal language for me. It felt good to be taken as one of the family, that was true, but since I barely understood what they were saying to me, I also felt kind of lonely. The only way to break out of this bubble, I thought, was to learn Estonian.

The next morning in Karksi started with leftovers. As soon as Epp and I sat down to the breakfast table, the plate of quivering *sült* came my way.

I tried to grab as much bread and cucumber slices as I could so that there would be no room for the *sült* on my plate. In trying to ward off the treacherous dish, I gobbed some brown mustard on my sandwich and stuck it in my mouth. Suddenly, a volcano of heat erupted on my tongue. My eyes watered and I began to cough violently.

"What's the matter?" Aap said.

"Justin doesn't eat *sült*," said Epp.

"He doesn't eat *sült*?!" said Eva. "Why not?"

I downed a glass of milk and poured another, trying to get rid of the burning sensation.

"My plate is full," I squeaked to Eva.

"Don't lie," Epp said.

Andres, chewing on a cucumber, sat at the end of the table, looked as if he was going to say something, but did not.

"Well, if he doesn't want the *sült*, it's ok with me," Pets grinned. "It means more for us."

I wiped a tear from my eye and examined the yellow tube of mustard. *Kange*, it read.

"What does *kange* mean?" I gasped to Epp.

"He also eats his buckwheat porridge with sugar," Epp announced. "And with raisins."

Aap looked away from his plate. "I think I lost my appetite," he said.

"Can somebody please tell me what *kange* means?" I squeaked again. My mouth was still on fire from the mustard.

"He puts raisins and sugar in his buckwheat porridge?" said Eva. "That's really gross."

I downed another cup of milk and panted in exhaustion. The burning sensation mellowed. The worst was over.

"You know, if Justin doesn't want to eat *sült*, we have plenty of leftover cake," Eva suggested. "Let me go get him some."

161

Andres raised an eyebrow, said "mmmmm," and took another sip of his coffee. I searched a nearby bookshelf for an Estonian-English dictionary and pulled one out. *Kange* meant 'strong' in Estonian. That's what I thought.

Simona skipped into the kitchen and grabbed my hand.

"Justin, *tule ülemisele korrusele*˙!"

"What?" I tried to parse all those syllables, but my Estonian was still at a beginner's level.

"*Ül-e-mi-se-le kor-ru-se-le*!"

I looked at Epp for help.

"It means 'upstairs'," she said.

"Your word for 'upstairs' is nine syllables long? How am I ever going to become fluent in this language?"

Epp smiled and forked another gob of *sült* in her mouth.

"We don't have time to go upstairs," she said to Simona. "We have to go and show Justin the castle ruins."

"Do you know what local people call it?" asked Epp. "The 'Estonian Switzerland'."

Andres and Tiiu's house sat atop of a plateau that sloped down into a nearby valley crossed by a river. A second hill rose up again into the "city" of Karksi-Nuia, or just "Nuia" as everyone around me called it.

Given that Estonia's tallest "mountain" – Suur Munamägi in Võru County – was really just a big hill, only 318 meters

---

˙   'Come upstairs!' in Estonian.

www.SNAPFISH.COM
64189161 174 5-97470 C3   03/11/08

above sea level, maybe, if I was shorter, the sloping hills and valleys of Karksi-Nuia could resemble some flat part of Switzerland in winter. But "Estonian Switzerland" did sound charming, even if it was another exaggeration. Besides, it was only an hour's drive from "Athens on the Emajõgi", Tartu.

We had walked to this knoll from Nuia's central bus stop. It only took about 10 minutes to get there by bus from Andres and Tiiu's house.

The air in Nuia was cold. I could feel the cold air leaking through ever tiny gap in my clothing. My joints ached, but Epp and Aap trudged on, as if it were a balmy day in July.

Outside the bus station, a pair of teenagers swept by on skis.

"People ski in town?" I was amazed.

"Why not," said Epp. "It is the fastest way to get from one place to the other, isn't it?"

I imagined how great it must feel to ski from your house to the local store, buy a couple bags of milk, throw them over your shoulder, strap on your skis, and glide all the way back home. Pure freedom.

From the crest of the hill we walked to the walls of an ancient castle. Even in the sunlight they looked cold, gray, and ominous.

"The German knights built this castle when they came," said Epp. "They say the Germans walled in a local woman when they built the castle. And during the next centuries, that's when we got our German blood."

In my imagination, this local woman looked just like Epp. I could hear her there sobbing in the stone walls of the Nuia castle, starving or suffocating to death.

"What do you mean you 'got your German blood?'"

"The manor owners had the right of first night," she said. "When an Estonian man got married, the German landlord had the right to have sex with his bride first; to take her virginity. You can imagine how many half-German kids were born that way."

What had happened in this country? It was a whole society that had internalized centuries and centuries of submission to cruelty. And they revealed it just as Epp or aunt Salme had: with the plain politeness of a good host or the clinical tone of a museum curator.

"I was baptised in that church," Epp gestured towards a tall Lutheran church's partially sunken tower. Plain and white, the old building sat surrounded by a grove of melancholic pine trees next to the ruins of the castle.

"But I thought you couldn't get baptized in the Soviet Union."

"You could in secret," she said. "My mom was baptized in secret. But I was actually baptized when I was 16."

"Why?"

"Because I wanted to be baptized. That was the year I found God."

Epp had a completely different relationship with God than I did. For her, he or she or it was shiny and new and growing more powerful every day. For me, God was about as welcoming as the intimidating Crucifix on my grandmother's wall. In Catholic kindergarten they told us that He knew everything we did, and was always watching. He loved us, we were assured, but we should fear Him because He might decide to teach us a lesson, with love as His ultimate intention, of course. After that, I could never pee alone without thinking God was watching me.

"You found God?"

"A lot of people found God in late 80s and early 90s here," Epp said. "It was the cool thing to do."

All this time, Epp's teenager brother Aap stood on the sidelines saying nothing. He wasn't threatening. He wasn't particularly happy. He was just like one of the trees. That's what so many of the Estonians were like, come to think of it. Walking trees.

Epp looked one last time at the old church and turned back towards the castle.

"Come on, let's go sledding," she said.

"But we don't have any sleds."

Epp didn't have time to hear me. Instead, she ran and dove, tumbling down the castle hill on her butt, towards one of the frozen creeks. "Whoo!" she screamed. Aap eagerly rolled afterward through the snow without making a sound.

I took out my digital camera to get a shot of them and took one or two before the whole camera shut down. What was wrong with it? I had just charged it the night before. Even the shutter wouldn't close. Then I realized that maybe digital cameras weren't designed for cold days like these in South Estonia.

"What's wrong?" yelled Epp from the bottom of the hill.

"I think my digital camera is frozen."

"Who cares?" her voice echoed. "Come on down." And with a running start I tumbled and slid down the hill.

THE WAR
BEGINS

*"My fellow citizens, events in Iraq have now reached
the final days of decision. For more than a decade, the
United States and other nations have pursued patient
and honorable efforts to disarm the Iraqi regime
without war."*

Backdropped by red, white, and blue, the American president
stood before a podium giving a final ultimatum to the Iraqi
leadership. We sat huddled around our new television set in
our Tallinn apartment.

Bush's nostrils flared with contempt for the Iraqi regime,
and I ate another potato. I ate a lot of potatoes these days. It
seemed as if every night I went to sleep with a rock pile of root
vegetables in my stomach.

I thought of Bush as the American president, rather than
just my president, because I wasn't quite sure of the link between me and him. I hadn't voted for him and I wasn't quite
convinced that he had won the election.

I had an American passport. Our apartment stood opposite the American embassy, and there was no other embassy in
this ice box called Tallinn that would consider me its own. All
those poor huddled masses in their black and gray coats and
hats would wait in a line outside the embassy in the bone-chill-
ing morning darkness just to get a visa to a place where I was
welcome. That much was true.

And if I went back to the Italian Embassy in Tallinn, telling that both of my grandfathers were Italians and begging for
them to take me in as some kind of long lost son, they would
surely tell me to come back after lunch. If came back after lunch,
they would have already started dinner. The Irish? Could a guy
named Petrone really pass for an Irishman, even if he had an
Irish grandma? And besides, they put ketchup on their pasta.

No, I was stuck with the Americans. Unless I decided to
naturalize as an Estonian. In which case, I would have to learn
the difference between *ostma*, *otsustama*, and *otsima*˙, before I
filed my application. And *suusatama*, *suitsetama*, and *sussuta-
ma*˙˙. Why did all these Estonian words sound the same?

"It's not just Estonian words," said Epp in defense of her native language. She squirted another dollop of sour cream on her
potatoes – she put sour cream on all her foods – and watched
the American president.

"The danger is clear: using chemical, biological or, one day,
nuclear weapons obtained with the help of Iraq, the terrorists
could fulfill their stated ambitions and kill thousands or hundreds
of thousands of innocent people in our country or any other."

˙   'to buy', 'to decide' and 'to search' in Estonian.
˙˙ 'to ski', 'to smoke' and 'to hush' in Estonian.

I thought about my friends who were in the military. Why had they joined? Mostly because it paid for their education. During the 90s, recruiters would show up at high schools and colleges telling potential new enlistees that they would never be put in harm's way. One had even tried to get me to enlist in college during the NATO bombing campaign against Serbia.

"My father was drafted," I had told the recruitment officer. "If he had gone to Vietnam I wouldn't be here."

My father had actually been stationed in West Germany on the Czech border. He had been there in 1968 when the Soviets crushed the Prague Spring. Still, many of his friends were sent to Vietnam. In Washington, DC, I had watched him choke up when he looked up their names on the wall of the Vietnam memorial. "Do me a favor, son," he had said. "Never, ever, join the military." His message stuck with me.

"Don't worry," the recruitment officer had chuckled that day. "Vietnam will never happen again. These days we just park our destroyers off the coast and lob missiles at them."

That had only been four years prior. Things had obviously changed.

❀ ❀ ❀

We bought a TV set so we could watch the war unfold. A used one was advertised in a district of Tallinn called Mustamäe. Mustamäe was the first of Estonia's post-war urban apartment districts, developed mostly in the 1960s. Its larger, more ominous offspring Õismäe and Lasnamäe would be constructed later. A song on *Vikerraadio* – the pensioner's radio station that we used to listen every morning – had gone like this: *Nüüd elan Mustamäel / Korter on aus ja hea...*

It was your classic postwar song, a song about new and prized material possessions. Even if the Estonians didn't have their flag or their independence anymore, they had their new flat in Mustamäe. To those families, still licking their wounds from the war and the deportations, it must have seemed like a lot.

Our trolley snaked ahead into a forboding complex of apartment blocks and, looking around, I wasn't sure if we had passed through a black hole somewhere back on Sõpruse Boulevard. In downtown Tallinn, I felt that both of my feet were firmly planted in the present. Free wireless signs were ubiquitous. The shops sold the newest athletic shoes and played the new tracks by Beyoncé and 50 Cent. But here in Mustamäe, I wasn't sure if I had taken a trolley back to 1984.

Old ladies in dark coats scurried down mottled sidewalks and little kids pelted each other with icy snowballs under bare laundry lines. The piles of ice on the side of the road were black with exhaust. The cold air stank of fumes from passing cars, too, if you could breath in any air beyond the icy perimeters of your nostrils.

The TV seller who lived in this labyrinth was a birdlike middle-aged woman with closely-cropped black hair. Her name was Rebekah, and she seemed as non-threatening as her beige wallpaper. Rebekah spoke Estonian with a spicy Slavic accent, and welcomed us inside her apartment, that, other than

---

* 'Now we live in Mustamäe, our apartment is good and strong' in Estonian.

the fake linoleum 'wood paneled' floors, looked like it hadn't been refurbished since the late Soviet head of state Andropov's funeral.

"Would you like some tea and cookies?" she offered. How could we refuse? We undid our winter slops and sat down at her tiny kitchen table.

"So do you live here alone?" asked Epp.

"Yes," she said. "I have two boys. Well, two men. But one is in London and the other one is in Tel-Aviv."

She poured the tea and took a seat herself.

Epp and I glanced at the same object on her table. A small, metallic candleholder with room for seven candles.

"Oh, you are a Jew!" Epp said to the woman in Estonian. The woman straightened her back and blinked her eyes in slight irritation. She said nothing and poured us cups of hot tea.

"You know, I have been to Israel, even twice, for many weeks in a row," Epp said. "I was selling handicrafts in the market and writing articles. It was really interesting. I made several interviews with your people."

I shuffled uncomfortably in my chair as Rebekah said nothing in response to Epp's enthusiasm. In New York you just didn't walk up to people and exclaim: "You are a Jew!" Unless you were Epp. For Epp, an Estonian was an Estonian and a Jew was a Jew. She swore Estonians were not anti-semitic though; the most controversial thing they could say was that a tacky interior decorating job was "lit up like a Jewish Christmas tree."

"You know, Justin's college roommate was a Jew, isn't that right, Justin?"

Epp smiled to me, I nodded turgidly. "That's right," I said. "His name was Adam."

Rebekah nodded, as if she wished we'd just shut up.

"And Justin is from Long Island, New York, where there are lots of Jews," Epp continued. "They even celebrate all your holidays at school."

Our host blinked again and sipped her tea. In situations like these, I found it best to just say 'yes.'

Yes, Mustamäe lady, there are lots of Jews in Long Island, I thought of saying. *The congressman in our home district is even named Israel. Steve Israel. I have spun the dreidel. I've eaten potato latkes. I have sung songs at school concerts about Maccabees and menorahs. Why, I even dated a Jewish girl upon whose frontdoor was hung a sign: Shalom.*

Rebekah blinked and kept her silence, we finished our teas, and decided to take the TV. We exchanged a few hundred-kroon bills, and loaded the heavy brown box into the back of a cab.

As quietly as she had welcomed us in, Rebekah bid us goodbye.

❀ ❀ ❀

"I don't think your supposed to just come out and ask someone if she is a Jew," I told Epp in the car.

"Why not?"

"It's not polite."

"Do you think they are ashamed of being Jews?"

"No. It's just not how it works."

"What was wrong with her? You think she'd be happy we took an interest in her background."

"I know," I nodded. "She did have the menorah front and center."

"I don't get it," Epp said in frustration. "If I met someone who knew Estonians and who had been to Estonia, I would be happy. But she just seemed annoyed."

I sighed. "They are more sensitive about their identity, I guess."

"I'll tell you a secret," Epp continued after awhile.

"What?"

"Some Estonians actually think I am Jewish."

"Why?"

"Because when I was in Israel I met with a Holocaust sur-vivor who said the Estonian guards in the concentration camp near Tallinn were just as cruel as the Germans. Some people hated me for writing that article."

The cab driver glanced at us in the rearview mirror.

"Ssh," I said. "Let's talk about this at home."

❋ ❋ ❋

In our apartment the war continued.

"And all Iraqi military and civilian personnel should listen carefully to this warning: in any conflict, your fate will depend on your actions. Do not destroy oil wells, a source of wealth that belongs to the Iraqi people."

The war began on March 20. This time, Epp's younger brother Aap and his classmate Indrek from Viljandi had come to visit. We gathered around our used TV from Mustamäe, watching the show. Epp had made potatoes, again, for dinner.

The war had caused some arguments with my folks back in New York. "We're not invading them, we're liberating them," my mother argued in an e-mail.

"If you send an unprovoked army over a border with the mission to take over a country, that's an invasion," I fired back.

"You know why the ex-communist countries are taking part in this liberation," she wrote, "because they know what it's like to live without freedom."

I hated this dialog. No matter what, if you didn't think that Operation Iraqi Freedom would be a grand success, you were somehow on the side of Saddam Hussein. Even Estonia was joining the "Coalition of the Willing." But how could they seriously side with France's Jacques Chirac over Tony Blair and Bush. What had France done for Estonia recently?

"Justin, the Iraqi Republican Guard is a joke," my father assuaged me on the phone. "The whole country will fold in a few days – you'll see."

"I'm not worried about the Republican guard," I yelled, hesitating from bashing the phone against the wall. "It's what happens to all those guys with guns after the country falls. It'll be like 'Nam all over again'!"

"Justin, please."

"And kids from my high school class are going to have to go in there and get their limbs blown off. For what?"

"Trust me, Justin, it's not going to happen."

They didn't believe me, but Epp did, as much as she could feel my anguish. But the funny thing was how nobody else in Estonia talked about the beginning of the war. For Aap and Indrek, busy elbowing each other and making dirty jokes, the war was just another violent American TV show. And Epp's other relatives, Eva, Pets, Andres? They had nothing to say about it. In London, thousands had demonstrated against British participation. In Tallinn, all had been quiet.

Until I got a phone call one day.

"Justin, come home quick!" I could tell by the pitch of her voice that Epp was distressed.

"Why? What's going on?" I heard chaotic noise in the background.

"They're everywhere; destroying everything. They are right under our windows and I have no place to go! I don't think I can even get out of the house! They destroyed the car down the street."

"Who?"

"I don't know. Just come now!"

Hurrying home from the *Baltic Times* office, I worried about what was going on at the American embassy, across the street from our apartment. Maybe somebody had tried to storm it? Or worse?

I turned the corner to see a sea of wild youths corralled into a street off Kentmanni by police. They were creating an awful racket, banging on metal pots and screaming. Some wore gas masks, others carried signs. Were they genuine protestors or anarchists or just drunk kids? I didn't know, but those gas masks did look kind of scary.

Unfortunately, they had already trashed the embassy's security car by the time I got there, so I couldn't get a good action shot of the masked marauders slashing its tires or jumping on its hood, but I snapped a few photos for the newspaper anyway.

I returned to our apartment building and tried to enter the front door, but the police approached me and waved me away.

"But I live here!" I said.

The officer just shook his head. I would have to find another way in. I doubled back and took an alleyway to the back entrance. Fortunately, my keys worked here, too.

When I got inside our apartment, Epp grabbed me tight. She was shaking. "I was so worried. I have never seen anything like that before!"

"Eh, it was just a little political demonstration," I said, undoing my boots. "You should try living in Washington for awhile. It's a daily occurrence."

In April 2000 at my university in Washington, DC, a World Bank meeting was interrupted by days of protests. I took part as a legal observer – to avoid getting sprayed by tear gas – and watched as anarchists dressed in black picked up a telephone booth and destroyed it in the middle of the street. I had the sounds of helicopters stuck in my ears for days after that.

"Compared to what I have seen, this was nothing."

"Thank you for coming so quickly," Epp said again. "I couldn't stand that noise here alone." Down the street another police siren filled the air.

"Don't worry, it's just some kids," I said to her. "It could be worse. We could be in Baghdad."

❊ ❊ ❊

"Have they agreed to put you on payroll so that you can get a living permit?" Epp stood in the kitchen with her arms folded. It was the end of March, the war had now been raging for a week, and Baghdad still hadn't fallen. In a month's time, I would run out of my permitted 90 days in Estonia. After that, I would become illegal.

"They haven't gotten back to me," I told her. "They" meant both the language school and the newspaper. They both had promised to "take care of me" when I first started working for them.

"Well, ask them again, we're running out of time," Epp bristled. "I don't know what we're going to do if you don't get that permit. I can't live in your country for more than 90 days and you can't live in my country for more than 90 days. Where would we go then?"

We had talked about teaching English together in someplace like Chile or China. But before that, we had agreed to stay in Estonia until she finished her master's studies.

"I'll get it," I said. "Don't worry."

Later, I trudged over to the *Baltic Times* office. My story on the protest had made the front page, though we had to buy a good action shot of the protesters trashing that security car from Scanpix. Through the moist windows, I could see the snow begin to fall again. It was supposedly spring, but there had been no end to winter.

"So, how does it feel to be part of the most powerful country in the world?" Ivan asked as I walked into the room.

"I guess I feel the same way you feel," I shrugged.

"Me? I don't feel anything," he said, sipping his coffee. "I'm a reporter." And he was. He even had a sign above his desk that read, *Trust me, I'm a reporter.*

"As for me, I am glad that I'm here and not in the US," I said.

"Why's that?"

"Because everyone over there is brainwashed."

"The thing about war," said Ivan, "is that it's almost impossible not to be brainwashed."

"I think the American media is laying it on pretty thick."

"We saw the same thing with Serbia or Chechnya," Ivan said calmly, taking another sip of his coffee. "When a state is about to engage in a conflict," he shrugged, "they make a big enough propaganda batch for everyone."

BROKEN
APPLES

A young man with the weight of the world on his
shoulders walked in front of the Hotel Olümpia
on Liivalaia Street on a mid-April day
in Tallinn.

I had only walked for 10 minutes from the front door of our apartment building, but I felt inside as if I had been frozen for a thousand years. My sinewy muscles felt raw. My mole-like eyes remained in a protracted squint to keep out the blinding light of the uncompromising sun. And as I reached the kiosk across the street to buy one of my favorite chocolates, a sunbeam seemed to strike me softly on the neck to tell me that winter was finally over.

My eyes watered. "One chocolate, please," I said in Estonian and padded my wet eyes with the sleeve of my blue jacket. Why were my eyes so watery? Was I crying? I hadn't worn this jacket since we were in Italy last November. But that had been thousands of years ago.

I pushed the crumpled bills through the glass window onto the plastic money dish and the seller – a portly middle aged woman named Anastasia with fluorescent-orange hair– gleefully pushed the miniature chocolate with its Japanese-themed wrapping under the window.

"*Ileud päeva**!" Anastasia exclaimed. Her fat buttocks even bounced a bit when she said it. I wondered if she had had sex the night before for the first time in a long time. She seemed so content.

I wiped another hot tear from the corner of my eye and began to meditate on the huge questions on my mind. For a foreigner who had just lived through two-thirds of an Estonian winter, spring was a welcoming and surreal phenomenon.

❋ ❋ ❋

But spring also brought me some new problems.

"We'd really like to help you with your issue," said Gary, the editor of the *Baltic Times*, in response to my pleas for employment and assistance with obtaining a living permit. "But we just can't add more people to our official payroll. I'm sorry."

Nor could the language school, where my tardiness and, let's face it, terrible teaching skills, had tarnished any trust that existed between me and the chain-smoking middle aged female director.

---

* 'Have a nice day!' in Estonian.

"Do you have a certificate that says you can teach English?" she had said, lighting another cigarette.

"No, you know that I don't."

"Then officially we can't employ you."

"But you are employing me," I had insisted.

"Well, this is," she brushed her nicotine-stained hands, "off the books."

Depressed, I slunk home to Epp, who one night in bed informed me that she had arrived at a unique solution to our problem.

"Justin, I know this is going to seem a bit crazy but why don't we just get married?"

"Married?" I turned the word over in my mouth. "But how can we get married on such short notice? We've got to tell my parents, " my stomach cramped at the thought, "then announce the engagement, and then set the date. That could take months if not a year. That's how people get married, right? And my time runs out in weeks."

"We can just get married by the city," she said. "We'll just have a civil marriage. I mean, you yourself asked me to marry you, remember, in Ireland, in November."

"Of course, I know I did," I said, my voice grew tighter. "But I meant when we felt like doing it, not because we must do it; not just doing it to appease some bureaucracy."

"But why did you ask me to marry you then?"

"Because I really wanted to know if you would marry me. I just had to know."

"But weren't you serious about actually getting it done?"

"Not like this!" I exploded, tossing my hand in the air.

"Justin, calm down" Epp adopted her calm and rational Nordic woman voice. Oh, how I hated that voice and how it mocked my emotions! "Stop acting like a baby."

As soon as the word "baby" had passed her lips, a new volcano erupted. "Why do you have to say that? Why do you have to push my buttons like that?"

"Justin," she was still calm.

"Will you stop saying my name like that? It drives me nuts."

"What else am I supposed to call you? It is your name!"

"You don't have to call me anything."

"Well, whatever your name is, we have a problem," she said. "You are going to soon be illegal in this country. Your return ticket is not until June. There is no other way for you to get a living permit unless your employer agrees to help you get one or we get married. If you don't get one, you technically could be deported. Do you want to be deported?"

"I want to get married. But marriage is supposed to be romantic, not like this."

"It may not be the best circumstances, but we should do something."

"But this situation sucks."

"That's not what a man is supposed to say," she snapped. "A real man would put his arms around you and say he wants to get married and that's that. He would go out and buy champagne."

"How many times do I have to tell you? I do want to get married to you; just not this way!"

"Well, that is how it is!" Epp hit back. "Unless you find some other way to get a living permit, this is our only option."

She calmed down. I looked away.

"Just tell yourself that it's not the real thing then," Epp sighed. "One day when you are ready and feel like it, we can have a new celebration, right?"

"I can't believe you actually want to marry me anyway," I turned unhappily in our covers. "You have no idea what you are getting yourself into. Why do you want to get married to me of all people?"

Epp pulled the blanket off my body.

"Hey, what are you doing?"

"Get out!"

"What do you mean? It's time to go to sleep."

"Get out! I don't want to sleep next to you! I don't want to see you if you are going to have such a negative attitude about everything!"

"Will you please leave me alone?" I pleaded. "I'm tired. I want to go to sleep."

"Didn't you hear me?" she was angry. "Please leave my home immediately. The lease is in my name and I would like to be alone now!"

"Fine! fine!" I pulled on my trousers and then shoes. "Have it your way." I grabbed my jacket, and slammed the door on my way out the apartment into the cool spring air.

What the hell was I going to do? Here I was the very next day. I had returned home and slipped into bed and Epp and I both apologized to each other for our bad tempers.

But nothing had changed. There was still no solution to our dilemma.

I opened the chocolate and sat on a cement step outside the Hotel Olümpia and rubbed my sun-weary eyes. I had stopped crying. That was good.

The Hotel Olümpia had been built in 1980 as a "gift" from Moscow to Estonian SSR. It was part of a number of construction projects undertaken because Estonia had hosted some of the events of that year's Olympics, an Olympics that my country had boycotted. American sailors in Tallinn harbor? Over Jimmy Carter's dead body.

Epp even had a photo of her mother Aime wearing a shirt that read *Tallinn 80*. I wondered how many other people had that shirt. Maybe every Estonian got one. They all seemed to have the same furniture.

Aime and Andres were about 26 years old in that 1980 photo. And they had three little flat-nosed Estonian kids with them already: Epp, Eva, and Priit. Could you imagine, three kids by your mid-20s? Epp had said that all Saluveer men had been married with children by their 21st birthday. It seemed as if Andres had had a moustache since he was a toddler. I had seen no photo of him without one. Andres seemed to be man's man. But me? I wasn't quite sure what kind of man I was on days like these.

In my shoes, Andres would just get married and maybe say "mmmmm" when they asked him if he was willing to take this woman as his bride. He wouldn't throw a girlish fit over the unfairness of bureaucracy. No, he'd go out and buy champagne and some new tools to fix the plumbing in the bathroom while he was at it.

I decided to walk. On this day in Tallinn, the golden sun seemed to kiss every living creature with its rays. The snow melted away into small rivers and ponds that choked Tallinn's uneven sidewalks whose surfaces I was now seeing for the very first time.

Again, the water began to drip from my eyes. The black ice was not so invincible after all. Little old ladies with pick axes were now chopping up the last pieces and tossing them into the road where they were sure to melt in the sun. Why are those little old ladies chopping ice, I thought. Maybe they need the exercise?

The nearby trees swayed in the breeze, ebbing and flowing with the tide of the wind. I slid a piece of chocolate between my lips. Goddamn it was good. The best chocolate it seemed I had ever tasted. So good, it almost seemed erotic. Oh, what was this Estonian spring weather doing to my body? If only life was just me and this chocolate, I thought to myself. I could end it all here. Game over.

But the Tallinn traffic just kept passing me by. The salty tears on my face now dry, I finished my chocolate and made my way down to the bank to deposit the 500 kroons I had earned this week from teaching English lessons. To me it seemed like a huge sum. I was rich. I had five 100-kroon bills, each marked with the face of the Estonian poet Lydia Koidula. *Koidula looks sexy today*, I thought as I counted the bills again. *I bet she wrote some really good poetry.*

I floated into the bank on a sea of sunny euphoria. Here and there I spied the naked legs of young women eager to try out their summer fashions, even if it was only a few degrees on the other side of zero Celsius. The brightly lit room smelled sweetly of perfume and body odor.

I took number 76 and waited to be summoned to deposit my fortune of Koidulas. When the board on the wall blinked number 76, I floated to Bank Teller 3.

Even from across the counter, it seemed I was enveloped in a cloud of her essence. She smelled intoxicating. Her fingers were long, her arms were supple, and her heavy breasts stared out from behind her crisp tight white shirt like globed fruit.

The thick cables of her platinum hair hung caressed her shoulders, framing her beautiful, girlish face, thick lips, and eyes that betrayed her ancient reindeer herding forefathers and mothers.

"Can I help you?" she said in Estonian.

Her eyes hit me like search lights. I tried to speak, but no word would willingly jump from my lips. Who could say anything in the presence of this Baltic Aphrodite?

"Mmmm?" I managed to say.

She tried again to communicate with me in Russian, but that was no use. Finally, she switched to English. "Is there something I can help you with, sir?"

More of the air from her body passed over the counter. It filled my nostrils and I enjoyed every breath of it as I entered a deeper state of amorous semi-consciousness.

I rubbed my face and tried to speak again. "Yeah," I slurred. "I'm fine."

The teller smiled and seemed slightly embarrassed but confident. I probably wasn't the first idiot who couldn't make a deposit because he was overcome by her radiance.

I quickly eyed her chest once more. It looked as if one wrong move could force one of her shirt buttons to pop open, revealing her warm flesh. Why did young Estonian women have to wear such tight shirts?

"I used to dress that way, too," Epp had once whispered in my ear while catching me staring at a young woman at the cinema, "when I was 18."

The bank teller turned back towards me and I quickly made awkward eye contact again, which did about as much good as looking at any other part of her body. "It's true," I wanted to confess to her in sorrow. "We writers really are perverts."

I slid the five Koidulas over the counter and inserted my card into the machine to make sure the money went into the right account.

"It's a nice day today, isn't it?" she ventured, curling her thick lips. I could always tell when a woman liked me. Her pupils got bigger.

"Uh huh."

"Where are you from?"

"Uh, New York," I stuttered.

She handed me a printout showing my deposit and I managed to force my lips into something resembling a smile.

Then, as I held the delicate paper in my hands, I looked down at her soft fingers and noticed she wore a golden wedding band. I felt instant relief. Teller number 3 was married. She had a man somewhere else who had to put up with her overbearing sexuality. I sighed and my blood pressure slowly resided.

The teller smiled and tossed her golden hair back over her shoulder. I looked at her name tag. "Piret." Maybe she even had some kids at home back in Mustamäe.

"*Suur tänu*[*]," I said to her, still in a cloud of pheromones.

"*Nägemiseni*[**]*!*" I took a moment to remember her comforting voice. Maybe the memory of her would come in handy if I ever found myself in prison or the army.

I nodded politely. Then, I turned and got the hell out of the bank building.

"What is wrong with you?" I berated myself as I walked through Tallinn's lively, sunlit streets. "You can't even deposit money without slobbering over some poor woman. And you want to get married to Epp? Good luck."

❀ ❀ ❀

"So Gary couldn't help you with your living permit?" asked Steve, munching on a slice of pizza topped with pineapple and some other mysterious ingredients.

"No."

"Bummer."

It was sunny outside, but we were eating pizzas in the dry air of the *Baltic Times* office. We were all supposed to try a pizza from a different place in town and rate it for the purposes of the newspaper. I supposedly lucked out by getting to try the pizza from the most Italian joint in the Old Town. But the guy

---

[*] 'Thanks a lot' in Estonian.
[**] 'See you soon!' in Estonian.

who served me wasn't even Italian, he was from Argentina. And the toppings?

"This is not prosciutto. This is ham!" I lamented.

"So what?" said Ivan. "It's got to be better than mine."

I looked at the deep dish monstrosity masquerading as pizza on his plate. "Look", I explained. "I'm not saying their pizza is bad; it's just that they shouldn't say that it's topped with prosciutto when it's not prosciutto."

Steve and Ivan looked at me as if they had no idea about what I was talking and each sucked down another mouthful of sweet, acidic Coca Cola.

"What am I going to do without a living permit?" I asked them. "Steve, what did you do?"

"Well, I had an employer who helped me. Plus I own an apartment here."

"I don't think it's such a big deal if you live here illegally for some time," said Ivan. "It just means that when you leave in June they might not allow you to come back for awhile."

"For how long?"

"I don't know. Six months. A year maybe. Don't forget you are from the US, they would not dare to harass you for longer."

"But what happens if they find out before June?"

"Then they'll deport you to Finland or somewhere else," Ivan shrugged. "And believe me. You don't want to be deported. I've visited the jail where they keep those guys. It's in pretty bad shape."

"You should talk to Rick," said Steve. "I am sure there is a way around this. He knows all the tricks. He'll help you out."

"Who's Rick? Where is he from?" I asked.

"He's from New Jersey, I think."

"Oh, I've seen this guy at Hell Hunt pub," said Ivan. "He wears a black leather jacket, and he's always got a different girl on his arm."

"He's a real player," Steve agreed.

"The last time I saw Rick," laughed Ivan, "he was alone with something like five different girls."

"Blonde Estonian girls?" I said.

"Yeah, he thinks they're sexy. But I don't think they're that sexy."

"Why not?" asked Steve. "Estonian girls do have that ice queen thing going for them."

"And Estonian girls are to the point," I said in their defense. "You don't have to spend your time worrying about what they really think. If they like you, they'll let you know. If they want you to leave, they'll tell you to leave."

"You mean it isn't like being with American girls where you have to stay up all night, answering such important questions as 'but are we growing together the right way'?" Steve said. "You might have a point."

"Most Estonian girls are nice to look at, but they are just not sexy. They are too clinical. Russian girls on the other hand," Ivan paused in delight at the thought, "now *they* are sexy."

"Sexy until they hit 30," said Steve. "Then they turn into *babushkas*."

"Now, now," said Ivan, wagging a finger at Steve. "My girl's not a *babushka*. Yet."

"Well, I guess we are experts on this topic," I said, wiping a tear from my eye. It felt good to laugh.

"There must be something in this pizza," coughed Steve. "It's making me feel a little funny." Then his phone rang.

"Oh shit," he said, looking at the vibrating device. "It's her. I don't want to talk to her."

"Who?" I asked. "Pille?"

"No, Lyuba. Pille and I made up."

"You made up?" asked Ivan. "I thought you two didn't talk."

"We do now."

"Ugh, I've got to talk to her." Steve answered his phone, and I ate another slice of pizza.

"Yes. No. Well, I. Uh huh. Look, it's like I told you. Yeah? Let's talk later. Yes, I promise. Goodbye."

Steve tossed his mobile phone down into his pizza box. "Why can't she just leave me alone?"

"So much for Lyuba," said Ivan, looking at his friend's discarded mobile phone, now lying in a puddle of pizza grease.

"Looks like you're not the only one with troubles," Ivan turned to me. "Anyway, I wonder if they serve pizza in that deportation joint. What do you think, Justin?" Ivan smiled and took another bite.

❈ ❈ ❈

I paid the clerk for the champagne and bag of chocolate candy – Epp's favorite – and hurried home. When I entered the apartment, Epp was already lying on the bed in the dim light of our apartment, flipping through a worn copy of Jane Austen's *Sense and Sensibility*.

"How long have you been waiting there?" I asked.

"An hour or two."

"I'm sorry I am late."

"It's ok," she looked me up and down. "I can see you've been to the store."

"Honey," I said, placing the champagne on the bed stand. "I've been thinking."

"Did you come to propose to me?" she blushed.

"No. I already proposed to you."

"But for real this time?"

I frowned. "What do you mean for real? I already proposed in Ireland."

"Why aren't you smiling?"

"What do you mean?"

"I mean you don't look happy."

"Well, I mean the situation is..."

"So, you don't want to get married to me?" she said, wrinkling her brow. "You just do it because you have to?"

"No, it's not like that at all."

"It's not like that at all!" she mocked me in a childlike voice. She stood up and headed for the kitchen. "You think this situation sucks? I'll show you how I feel!"

In her nightgown, Epp grabbed a wine glass and launched it across the apartment. It struck the wall in a burst of chaotic noise and broke into shards which scattered all over the floor.

"What are you doing? What the hell is your problem?"

"This is my problem," Epp launched another wine glass against the wall. Then she picked up a bag of flour.

"Put it down!"

Epp looked at the bag of flour menacingly.

"Put it down."

She looked at the bag again and set it back on the counter.

"You're crazy," I said, shaking my head.

"So?" she huffed.

"You know we are going to have to clean that up."

"That's all you can think about? You came here to ask me to marry you, and now you are just standing there like a baby, waiting to clean up some broken glass. Why is it so?"

"Why do you have to say that?" I barked. "Why? I don't say things like that to you!"

"Say what? That's what you are. You look ridiculous," Epp gave me a disgusted look and walked back into the bedroom. "I don't want to see you. I don't want to be with you."

"I am not going anywhere. You can get the hell out."

"No, you can go," Epp said.

Instinctively, I reached for the first object I could find, which just happened to be an apple.

"What are you doing?" she said.

"This is what I think of this whole fucking situation," I wound up the apple and I let the fruit go. It struck the closet door, exploding into a thousand pieces that splattered across the room.

"What did you do to my apple?" she screamed.

"This," I said, winding up with another one. It exploded against the apartment wall in a spray of juice and pulp.

"Whoa," I said, surprised by the mess. "Who knew that apples could blow up like that?"

"You broke my apples!" Epp cried as I reached for a pear. "What are you doing?"

"Same as you," I said, putting my hand down. I slumped down against the kitchen counter and began to rub my tired face with my hands.

"I really wanted to eat those apples," Epp calmed.

"You must be kidding me."

Epp sighed and looked at the shattered glass and apple guts strewn across the floor. Her face showed a touch of remorse and then she let out a sad laugh. "I was acting like a real evil bitch, wasn't I?"

My eyes teared. "I can't believe those apples exploded like that." Then I also began to laugh.

"I'm sorry," Epp said, hugging me. I kissed her cheek and put my arm around her waist.

"We're just two idiots," she said. "Let's be friends."

"I know," I said, "and let's get married."

THE BOLD AND
THE BEAUTIFUL

---

*The Bold and the Beautiful first debuted in 1987.
As of my writing this, it is still the most watched
soap opera in the world. Despite these achievements,
the first time I ever saw it was in our Kentmanni
apartment in Tallinn on warm spring day.*

Epp was nestled on the floor in front of the TV peeling a grape-fruit. I had my nose in Rein Taagepera's book *Return to Independence*. But neither of us could concentrate, because we had to know one thing: whether or not Ridge Forrester, scion of the powerful fashion designing house Forrester Creations, could maintain his marriage to his psychiatrist wife Dr. Taylor Hayes after cheating on her with another woman.

"Come on, Doc, after all that's happened, after everything we've been through, let's just go to Saint Thomas and do it again. We'll charter a flight tomorrow and we can renew our vows," said Ridge. He had been trying to get Taylor to go with him to St. Thomas in the Caribbean for two episodes already.

"They are always renewing their vows," Epp informed me while sucking the juice out of another grapefruit.

We watched this show almost every day now. It had happened that only Epp would watch it while doing something else, like knitting a sweater or peeling potatoes, but the plot started to overcome me, too.

Ridge had fallen for Brooke Logan, but then Brooke left him for his father Eric, but then Brooke left Eric and now was married to Ridge's brother Thorne, although she still had eyes for Ridge. And of course there was Stephanie, Eric's dominating wife, the matriarch of the Forrester family, who was always trying to exert her influence on her sons' personal affairs.

According to Epp, *The Bold and the Beautiful* was one of the most watched shows in Estonia. Ridge Forrester and Brooke Logan had even toured Europe to connect with their adoring fans.

I imagined Ridge and Brooke and their personal cosmetologists arriving on the ferry, and then taking a limousine with a police escort to Freedom Square to treat their legions of female supporters to words of wisdom.

"After all this time; after everything we've been through," Ridge would say with gravitas into the microphone, "it's great to be here signing autographs in Tallinn, Estonia."

"They always say that line," Epp said, looking up from another dehydrated grapefruit. "After everything that's happened, after all we've been through." She opened another one. Soon we would have to return to the market to stock up on a few more kilos of fruits and vegetables. My shoulders were still sore from hauling the previous load.

To make things somewhat confusing, even though Tallinn and Helsinki were in the same time zone, they were showing different seasons of *The Bold and the Beautiful*.

In Estonia, we watched the 2001 season. Shortly after that episode would end, we would switch the channel and watch the 2003 season of the same show on the Finnish YLE-TV. Within just two years actors and actresses had been replaced, love triangles adjusted. Some characters had even returned from the dead. Who watching *The Bold and the Beautiful* could know in 2001 that Thorne's ex-wife Macy didn't really die in that car wreck, and was secretly living in Italy all this time? Through our TV set, Epp and I could reflect on a future that seemed almost unrecognizable.

If I had gone back but a year in time, though, I would suffer the same kind of future shock when shown my current life. I had been finishing up my senior year of university back then, itching to leave and, in my mind, finally start my life. From the vantage point of Tallinn, it seemed like a past that belonged to someone else.

My mother had urged me to get a master's at Columbia University, but I knew I didn't have the grades, and, besides, I had just spent most of my life in school. My first free choice as a free man was going to be to return to the prison I had just left? Not a chance.

"Don't worry about money!" she had said. "I'll pay for it." I didn't know where she was going to get the money to pay for Columbia University, but I told her honestly that school was not in my immediate future. I was yearning for adventure. My father, too, weighed in. He thought I should get a local newspaper job. But just a few days sitting in the hot Long Island traffic during my summer construction job killed that idea forever.

Even if they didn't understand me, they had to let me go. What were they going to do? Like it or not, adventuring at that point was my business, though, in retrospect, one could argue that I got even more adventure in the end than I had originally hoped for.

❋   ❋   ❋

The municipal building was of solemn gray construction with depressing windows for eyes, no doubt built during the Soviet era in an architectural style named after one dictator or the other.

Not far from that building, opposite the Stockmann department store stood a palatial building referred to as "Stalin's house" which was ornamented with balconies, presumably for viewing military parades, and topped with a red star.

When I first heard the name, "Stalin's house," I suspected the basement to be filled with unmarked graves and torture devices. The walls must have been covered by red posters purveying only the wise words of the Soviet Union's fearless leader, Josef Djugashvili, the man of steel. It may have been that way 50 years ago, but now it housed a fascist-looking casino and a bourgeois nationalist interior design boutique. If the great dictator were alive to see it, many people – from the casino croupiers to the interior designers – would no doubt have to be purged.

These are the kinds of things I thought about as I wandered around Tallinn. Helsinki had been built strong and with a uniform style in mind. Tallinn, in contrast, was a mishmash of every architectural design known to man. It was if every person built his house according to his or her own taste, without any regard for what the neighbors' house might look like. It was the capital city of a nation of me-first individualists.

The municipal hall's many floors made me feel small and anxious. It was time to initiate my marriage to Epp. We needed to obtain a contract, and I had brought along my trusty passport to prove I was who I claimed to be. I was nervous, but I also felt the hand of history at my back. *This*, I told myself, *is how things are meant to be.*

After a minute I spied Epp walking down the sidewalk. She was wearing her red jacket and her famous red pants. Her curly locks tussled in the wind and she smiled at me. I knew instantly that we were making the right choice. It was like being on the docks of Helsinki all over again. From all these throngs of women, I thought, this little crazy person was made for me.

"So, are you nervous?" she smiled, approaching me.

"Not at all," I kissed her. "Let's go inside."

Though my heart belonged to Epp, my body had continued to exist in a perpetual state of crisis since my encounter with the platinum blonde bank teller. I couldn't tell Epp about these feelings, though at the same time felt that I was lying to her.

My dilemma was that there were so many women in Tallinn that made me react the same way and there was something unusual with my body these days. It reacted too strongly to stimulation. Everything around me, from the trees to the food I ate, was more intense than usual. But the worst, the absolute worst, were the famously beautiful Estonian women.

Supposedly Estonian women were the country's greatest national resource. Finland had Nokia, the local media argued, but Estonia had babes. Estonian women did their best to comply with this edict. They spent fortunes on their hair and their clothes, creating an image of sultry northern womanhood. No man was strong enough to resist such temptation, even those men who were about to be wed.

Like a leopard seal on a beach full of penguins, I would walk through crowds of young ladies, my blood pressure rising. Their legs, their hair, their voices – it made me dizzy.

I had always considered myself an amorous person, but the desperation of the Nordic winter combined with the sudden onslaught of spring and its narcotic-like warm winds and sun overwhelmed my nervous system.

In any other situation, I might have enjoyed these feelings. Adjusting to the reality of marriage, though, caused some kind of deep internal conflict. *Is it right to feel this way?* I asked honestly of myself. *Is there something wrong with me?*

In these moments of self doubt, I reached for my partner. Epp, as crazy as she was, seemed like the most grounded person on Earth. She was a buoy in life's swirling oceans of fear. She could be counted on to trust the water at all times. I, meantime, staggered from one existential crisis to the next.

I told myself that spring was just mating season. All animals, from cute little bunnies to stinky alley cats and mangy dogs were overcome by the desire to perpetuate their species. Even though I could be reached by mobile phone, I was no different from a bunny or a dog, was I? But while the bunnies were content to hump away, I felt shameful. *It must be Catholic guilt,* I told myself. *Catholic guilt is what makes people like me feel the way we do.*

But Epp wasn't a Catholic. She was a Lutheran. Even if she didn't go to church, Protestantism was in her bones. For me, love was laid out like a banquet on a table, an orgy of foods to be consumed. For a Lutheran like Epp, though, love could only be reached via hard work and moderation.

On most nights, Epp would work past midnight. I could hear her clicking away at the keyboard and beg her to come to bed.

"What are you doing?" I would plead. "It's 2:30 in the morning!"

"It's like Tammsaare says," she would respond defensively. "You have to work and work and work and work even harder, and then you find love."

"Who's Tammsaare?"

"He is an Estonian author who writes about work!" she snapped. "Please go back to sleep. I am trying to get things done."

There was something a little perverted about the way she said the word "work", as if it wasn't really "work" but something really good, like "cake" or "massage." I understood work and I understood love. But I couldn't figure out how writing an article at 2 am helped the two to connect.

How could one find love through work? I was puzzled. I decided, though, that even if Epp was a workaholic Lutheran, she would need my support.

Besides, Lutherans didn't almost get heart attacks from bank tellers or secretaries with bulging cleavage or Tallinn teenage girls, even if they were Estonia's Nokia. No, Lutherans like Epp were too busy trying to plan the next day's schedule. Theirs was an orderly and somewhat more comforting life. I envied them.

Though I didn't understand it completely, I began to accept the implications of my choice in mate. I was marrying an Estonian, a kinswoman of the famous workaholic writer Anton Hansen Tammsaare. Our children one day would have a bit of Tammsaare in their blood too.

❀ ❀ ❀

"You must be Epp and Justin. Follow me, please." The municipal clerk, a small woman with short brown hair and rosy cheeks named Tiina, met us at the front desk and was ready to see us to discuss our impending marriage.

The woman's office desk was covered with various documents and books and brochures. She handed us a form, which we both filled out. It included information on our dates and places of birth, parent's dates and places of birth, occupations, and an affirmation of our desire to marry. I guiltily entered my parents' information, feeling that I was betraying their trust in me as a son by secretly marrying so far away from home and without their knowledge.

I wanted to tell them, but how could they ever understand? Mom probably thought this was a phase in my life, and that I would soon come to my sense and go to graduate school. Dad was still waiting for me to return and work for the local newspaper. They had the perspective of people who had already made their decisions in life. By signing my name on that paper in Tallinn, though, I had just made one of my own.

Epp spoke quickly to Tiina and I didn't understand everything they were saying. I handed the completed form back to her, and her eyes suddenly widened with suspicion.

"What is this name, Pet-ron-e?"

"It's my last name."

"So you are Italian?"

"No, I am an American with Italian roots."

Tiina turned to Epp.

"Are you sure you know everything about your future husband?" she said quietly.

"Sure," said Epp. "I have met his parents. He has no big secrets."

"I just want you to be certain that you want to marry this man, because it happens sometimes that these Italian men marry Estonian girls."

"But he's not Italian," Epp protested, "he's American."

"Well," Tiina continued to whisper in a cautious tone, "he looks Italian to me. For all you know, he could have a wife and a child back in Sicily."

"He's only 23 years old."

"Fine," said Tiina, drumming her fingers on the desk. "But I just wanted to make you aware of the consequences of your actions."

Tiina turned to look at me and smiled. I smiled back and tried not contain my laughter. In a way, I felt proud. I was interesting. I could have a wife and child in Sicily, you know. One could never be too careful with these Italians.

Tiina turned her face to the computer and attempted to select a date. We would be wed sometime in May.

"But can't you do it anytime sooner?" asked Epp. She didn't tell Tiina that I was about to become an illegal alien in Estonia, and wisely refrained from revealing any more about our problem.

"I'm sorry," said Tiina, quickly sucking in air. "May 13th? May 18th?"

"Definitely not the 13th! 13 is an unlucky number!" Epp scolded the clerk. "I have to do the numerology," said Epp, scratching down the numbers in her notebook. "Yes, mmhmm, I see, ok. Yes, the 18th is a good date for us. It will bring us lots of luck according to the numbers."

"The 18th it is," I gulped. This was no longer a hypothetical option. This was a real situation. As of May 18th I would be married and Epp Väljaots would become Epp Petrone. This time I reached and clutched her hand.

"I hope you didn't take offense that she said you have a wife and child in Sicily," Epp said on the way out of the office.

"Who knows, maybe I do. I have a wife named Maria and a little boy called Nunzio. A donkey, too."

The elevator door opened and a gorgeous woman in a low-hemmed shirt walked out. I sighed.

"What's wrong?" she asked.

"What do you mean?"

"I know when something is wrong with you," she said again. "So just tell me."

I studied Epp's face. I knew its lines so well that it almost seemed as if it were my own. Maybe this was what marriage was about. Growing into one being.

"Do you ever notice other people?" I asked, as the elevator began to descend.

"What do you mean?"

"That they are attractive?"

"Are you in love with someone else?" Epp looked worried.

"No," I said. "I just went to the bank one day and there was the girl with blonde hair and..."

"And what?"

"And she smelled good and she had this tight shirt and..."

"And?"

"And I gave her my 500 kroons and she put it in my bank account and I left."

"Ha! That's it?" said Epp.

"Well, yeah."

"Why are you telling me this?"

"Do you think it's normal for things like that to happen? You just go the bank and have some kind of hormonal attack?"

"Ha!" she reacted as if I were the most naïve person in the world. "Of course, it's normal to notice other people. That's just how things are."

"But it's not like I am romantically interested in them," I said. "I just notice them. I can't help but notice them."

"I am sure she was very beautiful. It's nothing to be ashamed about. "Anyway," she continued. "I have been in these stuffy relationships where you are only supposed to be thinking of the other person. It doesn't work."

"I guess it's hard to sustain that kind of interest in anything," I said.

"Actually, I like it that you notice other women," Epp smiled. "It makes me feel that you are not a prisoner of some illusion of me. That would be really annoying. It's better if we are together of our own free will."

"I still have no idea what you see in me. I am unsure of the future. I worry too much. I made only 500 kroons last week."

Epp smiled when I mentioned money. I guess it seemed so American. We exited the elevator and made our way out of the building.

"But you are not like most Estonian guys," she said. "You tell me you love me every day. An Estonian woman might wait her whole life to hear her man say it just once. All her life, she is cooking and cleaning and making cakes and working in the garden and doing laundry and then one special day, her husband gets drunk and tells her he loves her."

"Why don't they tell you they love you more often?"

"Because that's how Estonians are," Epp shrugged. "You should remember sometimes, that just as I am exotic for you, you are also exotic for me."

"But I do love you," I said, pushing the hair away from her face. "And, you have to admit, you are really beautiful."

"See, Tiina was right. You are my Italian husband."

❋ ❋ ❋

In the end, Dr. Taylor Hayes forgave Ridge Forrester for his infidelity. He was weak, he told her, and he just couldn't resist the overtures of one of the fashion designers.

Epp and I watched patiently as the two of them flew off to St. Thomas to renew their vows. The wedding scenes, Epp assured me, might stretch out over three or four episodes.

Unfortunately, during Ridge and Taylor's trip, one of their twin daughters was kidnapped by Jamaicans working for Ridge's jealous former lover. She was attempting to destroy his marriage and blackmail him back into a relationship. It took the whole season for Ridge and Taylor to be reunited with their daughter and, yes, we waited day by day for the outcome. By that point, I couldn't tell if the writing on the *The Bold and the Beautiful* was actually good, or if life in Estonia was just really boring.

PLAYING
BALL

The trouble was that after three months in Estonia,
I still had no real friends.

Steve from San Francisco was an acquaintance, but he seemed
too preoccupied with his tumultuous personal life to take me
under his wing.

Ivan at the *Baltic Times* office? He was more like a colleague.
Ivan went on ski trips to South Estonia with his real friends. I
was just some dead weight foreign freelancer at the office. Soon
I would move on, like all the other foreigners who came, worked
for the newspaper for some time, and left for good.

So I was lonely, and I reacted enthusiastically when Epp's
Uncle Tiit, an accomplished composer and musician, invited
me to come and play basketball. Tiit regularly played on ferries plying the route to Stockholm or Rostock, and had some
basic knowledge of a few foreign languages. Between my pidgin Estonian and his pidgin English, rich conversations could
be had.

Tiit picked me up at Kentmanni Street on a sunny April morning. I hadn't informed him yet that I sucked at basketball, but I decided that he wouldn't hold it against me, seeing that we would soon be family.

Tiit and his younger brother Andres, Epp's father, were a study in contrasts. Andres was a builder; Tiit a pianist. Andres lived in South Estonia and had chickens; Tiit lived in Tallinn and had a mean dog. Andres was sturdy and square; Tiit was lanky and rectangular. Both had moustaches, I concluded, to keep their upper lips warm in winter. How such different people managed to have the same exact mother and father was a mystery to me. Such are the wonders of genetics.

"So what kind of music do you like?" asked Tiit as the car sped towards the outskirts of the city.

"Bossa nova is my favorite."

"Ah," he said knowingly, "sweet jazz."

"Do you like sweet jazz?"

"I like all kinds of music." Tiit turned the car past a strip of shops and then into a complex of large white apartment blocks.

"You Americans are funny. You are always naming songs after places." Tiit had a deep, muddy South Estonian accent. I might eventually prove Ivan wrong and become fluent in Estonian, but I doubted if it was possible to become fluent in Tiit. He continued, mumbling: "I mean 'Sweet Home Alabama,' 'New York, New York,' 'California Girls.' All named after places."

"You mean you don't have songs about places in Estonia?"

"Not really," he answered.

"There's no "Sweet Home Kohtla-Järve?""

"No."

"There's no song about Lake Peipus Girls?"

"Not yet," Tiit cocked his eyebrow at me. "But we do have a song about Lasnamäe." He hummed the melody and beat out the rhythm on his steering wheel.

"Did you write that song?" I asked.

Tiit wrinkled his nose. "No, not that one," he said, perhaps irritated that he hadn't. "But I have written some others."

"Do you know the guy who wrote that song?"

"Justin, Estonia is so small," said Tiit. "If an Estonian owns a guitar, there's a good chance I know him."

❀ ❀ ❀

The team that Tiit and his friends had assembled on the basketball court was a welcome surprise for any person who was terrible at the sport. While Tiit looked to be in great shape, the rest of the men were deep in middle age in various stages of hair loss and flabbiness.

Supposedly Estonians were nuts about basketball. In the Soviet era, their team had won an all-union competition. It was the popular summer sport in Estonia, consuming people's attention until it was time to go cross-country skiing again. Sure, they weren't as successful as the Lithuanians. But nobody ever talked about Lithuania. For Estonians, their country was a little island separated from the rest of the world by water and self-obsession. From the vantage point of a basketball court on the edge of Tallinn, Lithuania was located somewhere between Belarus and Andalusia.

The leader of the team we would be playing against was named Rein. He wore a head band and looked like Benny Hill, with fluffy white tufts of hair poking out over his ears. Rein dribbled the ball while warming up as if he meant business, slowly, forcefully. Most of his body was lean and muscular. His stomach, though, was enormous. It looked as if he had swallowed a basketball or was about to give birth to another player. Good thing Rein's team agreed to play with their shirts on. Our team would play without shirts.

"I want you to guard Rein because you are taller than him," said Tiit.

"Sure thing," I said, trying to sound confident.

"Whatever you do, don't let him out of your sight," Tiit warned. "He plays rough."

"Don't worry," I smiled. "We can take these guys."

Out of breath and dripping with sweat I rushed to the far end of the court and attempted to catch some air before we would have to defend ourselves against the onslaught of the shirt squad.

I looked over to Tiit, who was already guarding his man and seemed as if he had barely broken a sweat. "Don't look at me," shouted Tiit, "Keep your eyes on Rein!"

Rein methodically worked his way down the court, steadily pumping the ball against the floor with his heavy meaty hands. His face was flush with stamina. His demon-like eyes were red with victory. Rein had now scored on me three times, but thanks to Tiit's jump shots, we were still ahead in the game. If I let Rein get by me one more time, though, I would once more have to suffer the pangs of emasculating humiliation. After all, I hadn't scored one point.

"Mart, up here; Jaak, over there!" Rein forcefully directed the other players with his free arm, slowly pushing me back towards the basket. My fellow skins adjusted, but as I turned to create more safe distance between Rein and me, he saw an opening and went through it, quickly dribbling the ball as he went in for the easy lay-up.

Our defensive positions collapsed into the center of the court. There were now at least five sweaty Estonians and one fatigued American clogging Rein's lane to the basket. But he didn't care. He snorted like a bull and drove forward.

One player fell backward and hooked my leg, dragging me down with him, but I would be damned if Benny Hill was going to score on me again. I fell forward into his massive, basketball sized stomach. Rein grunted and swung a heavy forearm in my direction, his knife-like elbow knocking into my chest.

Barely able to breath, I reached out and grabbed hold of the ball. Rein wrapped both of his arms around it, but was pushed forward by the collapsing bodies of three other players.

We lay writhing in sweat and body odor on the hard wooden court, fighting for possession of the basketball. We were still fighting a minute or two later when I noticed Tiit's mustached face looking down at us.

"Boys," he said, with a touch of humor. "Our time is up. The game is over now."

❀ ❀ ❀

Tiit saw that I was in bad shape on the way out the door. Even given the weight I had lost in Estonia, my lungs were still heavy with fluid from running the length of the court.

"You need something to drink," Tiit grunted in his heavy voice. "I'll buy you some *kali*."

"What's that?"

"It's like Estonian Coca Cola."

"Ok."

He handed a clerk at the gymnasium reception desk a 25 kroon note, and was rewarded with two plastic bottles of the mysterious, dark-colored *kali*.

Tiit undid the top of his bottle with a quick twist of his wrist and finished the whole thing in one gulp.

I eyed mine, and then attempted to do the same. As soon as the mysterious dark liquid hit my lips, I knew there had to be some kind of mistake. This was supposed to be Estonian Coca Cola, but it tasted like carbonated bread.

"It tastes good, eh?" said Tiit. "I always drink one after a game."

I coughed and decided to swallow the whole thing, just as Tiit had done. After quickly digesting the half liter of room temperature sugary foam, I paused for a second to wipe the sweat from my forehead. Then I let out one of the loudest burps of my life.

"I told you it was good," smiled Tiit. "Now you are becoming a real Estonian."

G U Y S
L I K E
R I C K

I held the phone receiver in my hands and carefully dialed the eight digits.

Nearby, Ivan banged out a piece on the new Juhan Parts government for the *Baltic Times*. His dark eyes seemed mesmerized by the blank document on the screen, a file that beckoned to be filled.

Heli meanwhile sat across the office, coffee in hand, a day-old edition of the newspaper before her. I took a deep breath and dialed the final number of Rick's mobile phone. It rang three times across the invisible telecommunications universe. Then a man picked up.

"Yeah?"

"Hi, Rick, this is..."

"Who is this?"

"My name is Justin, I am a friend of Ivan's"

"*Ivan?*"

"And Steve"

"Steve?" He sounded puzzled. "Oh, *San Francisco* Steve. I told him not to give out my number."

In the background I could hear women chatting in Estonian, glasses clinking, and light music playing on a stereo. It was 3 pm.

"I work with Steve at the paper. He said you could help me. He said you've been living here for awhile."

"Seven years."

"Well, I got here at the end of January and my three months are almost up. I just wanted to know if I overstay my time limit, do you think they'll try to deport me."

Rick snickered. "You're American, right?"

"Yeah."

"Then they're not going to do anything to you. The worst those Eastern European monkeys will do is put a pen mark in your passport that says you won't be allowed reentry for, like, six months."

"How did you manage to stay?"

"Pssh. I went to Helsinki and told 'em I lost my passport. I got a new traveler's passport the same day, and was back in Tallinn the next morning."

"But didn't they know it was you?"

"Those idiots don't know your name. They just record your passport number. But after you change it your passport has a different number."

"How did you know that?"

"I've been living in Europe for 20 years. I know a couple things."

"20 years?" I had thought that Rick was my age. Turned out he was a veteran expatriate, even more savvy than San Francisco Steve.

"I was at the Olympic Games in Sarajevo in '84, when you could walk down the street without getting your head blown off. That city was so cool. Who knew there'd be a war there?"

"So did you see the games?"

"Games? Heck no. I was too busy getting laid. Those Yugoslav bitches really know how to take care of you."

I paused a moment to digest the fact that Rick had just shared with me. Thanks to a series of feminist girlfriends, and Epp, who called herself a "post-feminist," the word "bitch" had been eliminated from my vocabulary.

Not knowing exactly how to respond, I decided to play along. "Don't you mean those *Bosnian* chicks?"

"Serbian? Bosnian? Croat? They're all the same," Rick chuckled.

"But Estonian girls are the best, right?"

Rick paused, as if he were looking around to make sure no one could hear him. "To tell you the truth," he whispered. "I'm a little bored with them."

"Why?" The question slipped from my lips, and I realized that, in my own way, I was interviewing Rick. It was a habit I picked up in journalism school. All my conversations eventually morphed into interviews. I just had to hear more, even if I already had started to hate Rick, for his attitude, for his vocabulary, and, especially, for saying bad things about Estonian women.

"The problem with Estonian chicks is that they are too big down there," said Rick. "Their asses are too big, I mean. And they are so cold. Latvian girls are much friendlier. Those bitches in Riga? Wow. But the hottest girls are farther east. My friend just got back from Ukraine. He said the chicks there are even hotter."

"Smaller asses?"

"You know it!"

Suddenly, our conversation was interrupted by a soft female voice.

"Who are you talking to?" I heard a woman purr in accented English to Rick. "No one, baby doll," I heard Rick say. "Just some American kid with passport trouble. I'll be off in a sec."

I heard the wet sounds of Rick sucking face with his cold, big-assed Estonian squeeze. She must have walked away after that, because he was thinking about Ukrainian girls a moment later.

"Like I was saying, I am seriously thinking about moving to Kiev. Every bitch is a model."

"But what about your job?"

"What job?"

"Isn't it hard for you to just pack it all up and move to Kiev?"

"I'm set."

"I don't understand."

"It means I have money. I am independently wealthy. I inherited the family fortune. I'm set."

If Rick's overt sexism and trash talking turned me off, the knowledge that he was rich turned mild dislike into passionate hatred. It wasn't every day that I really hated someone, but now I wanted to get back at him, to knock his rich, bitch-banging attitude down a bit, I searched for away to irritate Rick as much as he had irritated me.

"Well, if they are not going to deport me, then I should be ok."

"Like I said, all you have to do is go to Finland..."

"I don't need to lie to the embassy. I am getting married to an Estonian."

Rick sighed loudly. He was obviously unhappy with my decision.

"Married?" he grumbled. "Why the fuck would you want to do something stupid like that?"

"So we can stay together."

"Oh I see," Rick said. "You are going to save her."

"Save her? From what?"

"From Estonia, of course. All the bitches here want some American guy to save them."

"Well, technically, Rick, you could say that she is saving me, because I am the one who is going to be illegal."

"Look, kid, you called me."

"And you answered all of my questions."

"*Questions*, Scoop? You're not going to write something about our little chat are you?"

"Maybe," I lied.

"You don't know my last name," Rick squealed. "You don't know anything about me!"

"I know that you're a dick."

"Fuck you," Rick said. Then he hung up.

I looked again at the receiver in my hand and noticed it was shaking. I felt dirty after talking to Rick, as if I should go shower or gargle with mouthwash. I wanted to instantly erase what he had told me, but his words had already polluted my mind.

"Your friend Rick is an asshole," I said to Ivan.

"He's not my friend," Ivan protested, typing away at his keyboard, "but, yes, he is an asshole. Like a lot of Americans."

"If he's such a jerk, how does he manage to have so many girlfriends?"

"Are you kidding me?" said Ivan. "Women *love* jerks like him. They just can't resist."

I opened my mouth to say something but quickly changed my mind.

THF SPIRIT
OF TARTU

Epp loved writing. She wrote all day. She wrote all night. She told me often how one day she would achieve her goal – to be a writer. The fact that she already was one escaped her.

"But I want to be a real writer," Epp said. "Not just some journalist for a women's magazine."

Epp collected books on how to attain this lofty goal. Books with titles like *On Writing* or *Bestseller* or *Writing the Breakout Novel.*

Her fixation seemed silly to me. Why would you read a book on how to write? Didn't you just open your desk drawer, pull out a bottle of whiskey, or open up a bottle of wine? Still, Epp's love of the written word was contagious. Within a few months of living together in Tallinn, I had finished off more books than I had read in a long time. Anything from Bill Bryson's *Neither Here nor There* to the *Search for the Panchen Lama.*

In fact, her bookshelves were littered with spiritually-themed books. The treatises on Buddhism gave way to the Bhagavad Gita, the wise words of Sai Baba, and even a book on the occult. These were conduits for seeing reincarnated souls, achieving total consciousness, or communicating with the dead – things I thought most people didn't do in their daily lives.

Many Estonians like Epp seemed to embrace eastern philosophies. One day, for instance, I spied a wallet-sized photo of Sai Baba and his divine afro in a lady's purse as she paid for her groceries. And who could ignore the shorn Hare Krishnas who stared at you with enlightened eyes in Tammsaare Park?

It was true that when I met Epp in Helsinki I feared at times that I might levitate. *She has some hidden powers*, I thought at the time. *Maybe she is in touch with the Other Side.* I enjoyed the idea of being seduced by a woman like that. Even Arnold Schwarzenegger's character in *Conan the Barbarian* – a fearsome gladiator who in one scene slew a pack of wolves and ate them for dinner – had been seduced by a witch in the film, one I had seen many times as a child. Rock singer Jim Morrison had had an affair with a witch too, or at least Val Kilmer did in the Oliver Stone movie about his life. Coupling with the occult was what happened to cool guys in search of something. All other women were but mere mortals. They worried about their nails. Witches worried about the Other Side.

Epp hadn't always been a witch. She had also once been a little innocent-looking Estonian girl in countryside. I had seen photos. I had proof. What had triggered her spiritual quest, the one that led her to seek comfort in an ashram shepherded by some old fart with an afro who claimed to be an incarnation of God? I had had personal problems, too, but I didn't wind up meditating in India or seeing Sai Baba in my dreams. Was it her mom's death or her divorce? Maybe people were just different.

"Have you ever tried to communicate with the other side?" Epp asked me one day in our bedroom. I was thumbing through the *Dictionary of the Occult*.

"One time when I was studying in Denmark I tried," I answered. "It was cold and rainy. I was depressed and feverish. I couldn't get out of bed for days. I missed two weeks of classes. And I was walking one day and found a church."

"You went in?"

"No, it was locked. But I leaned on the outside tower, on the old stones. I figured that maybe somebody important had once prayed there too, like Søren Kierkegaard. And I asked God for help."

"And did he send you a sign?"

"No."

"So what did you do?"

"I gave up and went and bought a falafel from a street vendor. Why are you asking me this?"

"When I was in college we tried to contact the spirits," Epp said.

"*Ouija* boards?"

"I used to do it with some friends, but it got so scary that I stopped."

"I could never use those boards," I said. "I just couldn't help myself from pushing it to say stuff and trying to scare my friends."

"Well, I never pushed," said Epp. "Most spirits we met were good, but sometimes you meet a bad one."

"What do you mean?"

Epp looked around the room. "It's best not to talk about it," she said. "I don't want to invite one into our lives... But I bet you did get better after you went to the church," she continued.

"About a week later, I did. I started eating again. I even made some new friends. When I think about my life in Denmark, it's always taking place after this time – when I had friends and felt healthy."

"I think we all have to go through these kinds of things in order to get where we are. My friend Toomas knows all about good energy and bad energy. That's why I started seeing him."

"Toomas?"

"He's a witch."

"How do you become friends with a witch?"

"Ha! There are lots of witches in Estonia," said Epp. "Estonians never really accepted Christianity. In the old days, every village would have its own witch. Witches even compete against each other. They are like celebrities. But Toomas stays out of the newspapers. He just helps people."

I wanted to believe her but couldn't. I had attempted to contact God when I was really desperate. On that day, He was somewhere far away from my reality. Epp must have been hoodwinked. There really was no Other Side. We thought we were speaking beyond our terrestrial forms, but we were just talking to ourselves. Still, witches *were* at least interesting, even if they were all frauds.

"Do you think I could meet him?" I asked, humoring her.

"We are going to see him this weekend," said Epp. "We have an invitation for Saturday night."

❀ ❀ ❀

Our bus rolled into Tartu about 11 in the morning. I was in a black mood. It had been a long week, and even two student's coffees couldn't rouse me from my usual morning fog.

I was an evening person, but Epp was a morning person. As soon as her Estonian foot hit the wooden floor of our Kentmanni apartment, the day began. Coffees were made, bags were packed, and appointments were confirmed. She had raw energy but she couldn't drag me with her to the bus station on time. We were late and missed our ride. We would have to take the bus that left a half hour later.

For a good 15 minutes I had to hear about how irresponsible and lazy I was, how I had ruined all her plans, and how we were going to be late. Late! It was grounds for execution in some countries.

"You should relax," I commanded her. "Just trust the water."

"It's not funny," she scowled. "You have to grow up. People in Estonia are on time. Eva is expecting us."

I buried my nose in a book, Epp flipped through a magazine. Slowly the tension resided. Minutes later we were holding hands.

Eva didn't seem to care she cared when we arrived at her door. She was boiling potatoes. Pets was away doing some freelance electric work to make ends meet while he awaited his call to the sea. Pets' gray-haired mother, known to all as Mamma, was in her room in the apartment, captivated by the plot of a Venezuelan soap opera, where both the male and female characters' voices were dubbed by the same monotone Estonian guy.

Epp dropped our bags in the hallway and told Eva that she had to go do an interview. But what could Justin do in the meantime?

"It's a nice day. He can take Simona out for a walk," Eva suggested.

"Do you think you can handle that?" Epp asked me.

"Sure, but my Estonian isn't so good."

"That's ok. Simona can teach you."

Epp had a busy schedule, but our tardiness hadn't slowed her down. She was interviewing different Estonian women about their opinions of women's magazines, for her master's paper. Epp was supposed to meet Ruta at 10.30, then Kaili at 11.30, and finally Sirje at 12.30. But Ruta had to go to Tallinn at the last minute, so Epp would meet her later in the week.

This was Estonia's mobile-phone facilitated lifestyle, a never-ending relay race of meetings made or postponed by text message so that each person could squeeze every useful moment out of the day. I wondered how people did it in Aunt Salme's time.

"They usually made appointments in person because the KGB was always listening to people's phone calls," Epp told me. "And they always kept them and *were on time.*"

Even though it was spring, Eva bundled little Simona up with a winter jacket, a hat, mittens, and a scarf. Simona's hat was covered by little hearts, while her scarf had a cute image of a kitten stitched into it. With her flowing blonde hair and blue eyes, she looked like a commercial for something wholesome, like milk.

Epp left with us to go to her first appointment. She was so happy to be free of all of the obstacles that had stood between her and work. And she was right. I did need to be more responsible. It was as my media law professor had told me in college: "I can always tell when you show up for class, Justin, because I hear the door slam behind my back 10 minutes after I start my lecture."

"Try to be back by two," Eva said as we left the apartment. "I am making cutlets, potatoes, and a cake."

The April sun had killed the last of the snow in Tartu, and only a few patches of winter lay in the shadows of Gothic steeples and Baroque eaves. Like busy ants, Estonian construction workers were resuming the restoration of St. John's Church.

Epp told Simona that I would be in charge for the next hour and left. Simona didn't say much, considering her little mouth was hidden under a fluffy scarf. We decided to head off towards the town hall square.

Tartu was different from Tallinn. But what was it that made it so different? Young hip men and women paraded down Rüütli Street – girls with hair dyed black, pierced noses and flowing granny dresses; guys with scruffy beards, smart-looking spectacles, and berets. Where were the conservative politicians and bankers with their smart suits and luxury cars?

It's like being in Haight Ashbury, San Francisco or the East Village, New York, I thought. I'm surrounded by punks and hippies. This must have been that legendary spirit of Tartu they talked about in the guidebooks, that hidden ingredient that made Estonian country folk blossom into modernist poets and transcendental gurus.

Epp had been a student here. It had been in this potent mix of free love and student days that Epp had developed from a farm girl into a roving bohemian. I wondered what would happen when Simona grew up. How long would it be before she was among those crowds of kids drinking beer near the Jaan Tõnisson statue, the one that read '1868–1941?' because nobody knew exactly when or where the Soviets had executed him.

Simona and I walked over the arched cement bridge across from Town Hall Square, and everything seemed fine. She didn't say much, and when she did, I pretended to understand her. Babysitting was easy. Simona was a good little girl. We paused to look down at the flowing Emajõgi waters, revivified by the melting snow. Suddenly, Simona spied something below in the river and sprinted ahead.

"Simona," I cried in my best Estonian. "Where are you going?"

Simona didn't look back. She turned the corner off the bridge, and set off down abandoned, treacherous-looking steps that rambled to the water's edge. Here on the broken cement, the ice had not yet entirely melted. Simona skipped down to the river's edge, while I slid behind.

"Simona, come back here right now," I demanded as she crept along a crumbling cement platform towards the frigid, fast-moving Emajõgi. The river was almost twice as high as it usually was. I had no idea what to do if Simona fell in.

Jump in to save her? Didn't people usually die trying to rescue others?

"Simona, get back here now!" She hooked a long piece of drift wood with her little mitten and began to tug.

"Simona!"

"Go away!" she screamed. I moved cautiously behind her and helped grab the drift wood out of her hands.

"Give it to me. Give it to me!" She was hysterical. Simona jumped up and down, crying for the thing that had caught her eye. I looked back at the dark river water and moved away slowly towards higher land. Simona followed me away from the river's edge.

"If you want this wood," I told her, "you're going to have to do what I say." I did not try to speak in Estonian anymore.

Simona gave me a nasty look and followed me back up the slippery steps.

"That's better," I said, handing the wood to her at the top. It was, lengthwise, even taller than she was. *Maybe if she's weighed down by driftwood*, I schemed, *she won't escape like that again.*

We walked towards the supermarket through a wooded park. Here and there, Simona would find the broken boughs of trees that had come down with the snow melt and add them to her bundle of wood. Some branches were twice as long as she was tall. We were a preposterous sight – a clumsy ogre following a small girl with an armful of deadly spears through downtown Tartu. The bundle got bigger and bigger as I pondered what to do. I didn't want another scene, but this was getting out of control.

So, I decided to take away Simona's wood collection. We were pretty far from her home now. I couldn't imagine us making it back with all these sticks. I reached down to pull them away, but the little wholesome elf clung tightly to them.

"At least let me break them in half," I pleaded. "Then it will be easier for you to carry."

I tugged at the tallest stick, which came up to my shoulders.

"Let go," she cried. "These are mine."

"You are not going to the store with these sticks," I lectured. "Either we break them down to something smaller, or you leave them all here."

Simona wrapped her arms around the wood and fell to the ground, crying. That was it. I was not about to be bossed around by someone one quarter of my height. I was Simona's chaperone, and I got to decide which sticks we took home and in what condition. I reached down and pulled the biggest branch out from her grasp. Then I broke it over my knee.

When the branch snapped, Simona screamed as if had broken her leg or arm. People on the other side of the busy avenue looked in our direction. An old woman passing by intervened.

She had curly white hair, wore a thick purple coat, and had thighs like oak trees. She was what Epp would call a *memm*[*]. When these old *memm*s were children in the 1930s, Konstantin Päts was president. When they were adults, it was Josef Stalin or Nikita Khrushchev who was in charge. Now, they spent their twilight years under the watchful stare of newly-elected Prime Minister Juhan 'Choose Order' Parts. What did they think about all this? Who knew? They were too busy

---

[*]   'An old lady' in Estonian.

making cutlets and potatoes and watching Venezuelan soap operas.

"Hello, sweety," Memm said to Simona. "Why don't you give those branches to your daddy?"

"He's not my daddy," Simona growled.

"I'm her uncle," I told Memm.

"Just give those branches here. Granny won't hurt you."

Simona pulled the branches tighter. "Give them here," Memm began to tug.

"No!" Simona cried.

"What a determined little girl," Memm gasped. She tugged with all her might. "I said give them here!"

They went back and forth, pulling on the branches, as traffic whizzed by. At last Simona's grip loosened. Memm pulled the sticks out and tossed them into a nearby bush with satisfaction.

"There," she brushed her hands as Simona sulked. I thanked the old lady. "It was nothing," she said. "Sometimes young parents need help."

"I am not her parent." Memm ignored me, picked up her black purse, and went on her way.

Simona was miserable for the rest of the walk home. I bought her a Vanilla Ninja ice cream at the store to console her for the loss of her wood collection.

Later, when Eva, Epp, Mamma, Simona, and I all sat down to an afternoon feast of cutlets and potatoes, I related my story.

"Simona, why did you do that?" Epp scolded her niece. "You know Justin doesn't speak Estonian very well."

"But Daddy and I always do it together," she pounded her little fists on the table. "And Justin broke my favorite branch!"

"Pets likes to take Simona to get firewood," Eva informed us. "*He* never has any problems with her."

I felt ashamed. Here I was, 23 years old, and I couldn't even watch a little girl for an hour without her almost falling in a river or getting into a wrestling match with an old lady on a sidewalk. I was unfit for parenthood.

"I bought her some ice cream to make up for it," I said.

"*Ice cream*? Before lunch?" asked Epp. "You know you aren't supposed to do that."

"I'm not?"

"It ruins the child's appetite," Mamma chimed in.

I decided to shut up and drink my milk.

Supilinn was a neighborhood within five minutes' walk from Eva and Pets' front door, but the narrow lanes that led to what Epp described as a "wooden slum" transported you into a new Estonia, an Estonia of rainbow-colored wooden shanties, smoggy furnaces, and overgrown vegetable patches.

This was the epicenter of the spirit of Tartu, a neighborhood affordable enough to house all of the city's poets, drunks, revolutionaries, and car thieves. Estonian Jack Kerouacs and Jerry Garcias discussed Dadaism in crooked alleys and wild little girls with balloons and painted faces rolled by on skates.

Epp, Simona, and I moved towards the roar of rock bands, the eye of this particular 'Spirit of Tartu.' It was Supilinn Days – an annual festival where all of Tartu's new bohemians gathered to rock out, read poetry, and reflect on the mystical journey of life.

When the Germans and Soviets blew central Tartu to bits, they left Supilinn intact. Before the 19th century, the only residents of this flat, marshy riverside plateau were geese and frogs, Epp told me. As the river receded, a whole neighborhood arose at the time of the first Estonian Awakening, with street names like *Marja, Herne, Kartuli, Oa**...

"I know a German guy who thought that building was marked 'Zero A,'" Epp said of the Oa Street sign. "He couldn't believe that we start buildings with the number zero in Estonia. It was even harder to convince him that Oa is a word."

"Why are most of the streets unpaved?" I asked her. "Doesn't the city have the money to pave them?"

"Because the people here like the streets the way they are. Unpaved streets are so much more romantic."

We made our way to the center of the celebration. A group of young guys banged away on their instruments on stage, guitar lines reverberating, singer howling, drums thundering, sounding like the Estonian step-child of U2 and the Sex Pistols.

"This is great," I told Epp. "Too bad they don't have stuff like this in Tallinn."

"Do you want to get some pancakes?" Epp motioned towards a line of people who looked like extras from the Beatles' *Magical Mystery Tour*.

"I had too many cutlets," I hiccupped. "Maybe Simona wants some? Simona?"

We both looked around, but Simona was nowhere to be found.

---

* 'Berry, Pea, Potato, Bean' in Estonian.

"Where did she go?" said Epp. "She always does things like this!"

"Simona!" I cried out and looked around at the crowds. It was no use. No one could hear me in the din of the Estonian Sex Pistols. A group of scruffy guys that looked like the Tartu chapter of the Hells Angels passed us by. "Where could she be?" I was worried. "You don't think someone took her, do you?"

"Let's split up," said Epp. "You walk closer to the street and I'll go check down by the river. She must be somewhere."

How was I going to find a blonde little girl in a country full of blonde little girls? I elbowed through the crowds. Here stood a house that had permanently shifted 15 degrees to one side. Half the roof was black with soot from a fire. Two of the upstairs windows were broken. Inside I heard a woman cry out a boy's name:

"Raul?"

No answer.

"Raul?"

No answer.

"Raul! What are you doing? What is your damn problem?"

Then I heard a slap and a little boy began to cry from somewhere inside the crooked dwelling.

What would a 19th century wooden ghetto be without a little domestic violence, I thought.

"What will you do when the world ends?" an old woman interrupted my thoughts. She had wavy gray hair and must have been standing beside me for some time.

"Excuse me? I need to go!" I searched the crowd of people behind her for Simona.

"There will be two groups," she said, staring at me with convincing gray eyes. "One will survive. One will disappear. Which side will you be on?"

"The surviving side, I guess." I looked in another direction, trying not to be distracted by the woman.

"Then you will have to join us." The old woman placed a piece of paper in my hand. There were pictures of smiling people of all ethnic backgrounds holding hands and walking into the sunlight. The fine text at the bottom of the flyer read: *Watch Tower Bible and Tract Society of Pennsylvania*. She was a Jehovah's Witness.

"We are meeting every Saturday," she said. "The address is on the bottom of this paper."

"Ok, but, listen, I really have to go!"

"What nationality are you?" she peered into my eyes. "Are you a Russian?"

"No, American," I told her. Where was Simona?

"American? And you speak Estonian already? Why, there are people who have been living here for 50 years who can't say one word."

"I'll show this to my wife. Maybe she'll be interested. She likes God." The old Jehovah's Witness looked pleased and walked on to another unsuspecting pedestrian.

I checked every face of every person between the pancake line and Oa Street, but I couldn't find Eva and Pets' little girl. If Simona had been kidnapped by the Tartu chapter of the Hells Angels, she was long gone. I decided to head back to where I left Epp.

"Jus-tin!" Epp called as I approached the spot. She was waving her arm in a thicket of locals. One of them had a water pipe tucked under his tattooed arm. "I found her." Epp pointed down towards the little mischievous elf. "She's ok!"

I felt instant relief and jogged over to Epp and Simona. "Where was she? Where did she go?"

"She was with her friend Laura and Laura's mother down by the river," Epp said. "She saw them when we got here and she took off without telling anyone. She's already said that she's sorry."

"I just wanted to play with my friend," Simona whined. She looked exhausted. Her short-won period of independence had been snuffed out again by meddling adults.

Later on the pancake line, I pulled Epp aside and whispered in her ear. "Honey, I love you, but maybe it's best if we wait awhile before we have kids."

"I agree," Epp was beautiful in the sunlight. "We still have to go on many more adventures before it's time to settle down."

"Now you will get to see how rich people lived in Soviet times." Epp was telling me more about Toomas the witch. Our taxi sped through the dusky streets towards Annelinn – Tartu's version of Mustamäe, also constructed in the late 1960s.

"He's a rich witch?"

"He was the manager of one factory, so he got a nice big apartment. Back then, people wanted to live in Annelinn."

I peered out at the labyrinth of cement boxes, their evening lights just starting to come on. "Why?"

"Nobody wanted to live in a wooden slum in those days. They wanted refrigerators and coffee grinders and vacuum cleaners and TV sets and, if you were really lucky, a car."

"Does Toomas have a car?"

"I am sure he's had one most of his life."

When we pulled into the maze of orange-colored apartment houses, somewhat cleaner and less threatening than Tallinn's, we were met with a challenge. Epp knew that Toomas lived in Annelinn. She just had forgotten where.

"I am pretty sure it's this house," she said, "but they all look so similar."

"He could be in any one of these apartments. It could take us all night to find him," I said.

"Wait. I have an idea." Epp proudly pulled out her mobile. "I have his number."

Toomas answered his phone and directed us to the right building and apartment number. We took a creaking elevator up, and I made sure to check the inspection date, listed in Estonian next to Russian language instructions.

Epp and I walked to the apartment door and rang the bell. In a second, the door swung open and we entered.

Toomas did not look anything like a witch. I thought witches looked like Merlin or Gandalf – old wise men with long flowing beards and robes. But those were wizards anyway. Toomas the witch wore a tight t-shirt with a golden smiley face on it, blue jeans, and had closely cropped gray hair.

Epp hugged Toomas and told him she was happy to see him. I gave my hand and he shook it. He didn't say much, but he wore a bemused expression, as if he was trying his hardest to suppress overwhelming currents of laughter.

"I hope you like fish," he said, "because we'll be eating to-night."

So this is what a rich Soviet person's home looks like? I took in the interior design. Over all doorways were hung plastic beads. The walls of the main corridor were papered with images of beaches and huge palm trees. Toomas is just a big kid, I deduced. No other kind of man would have palm tree wallpaper.

"He used to just be an average guy," Epp said as we walked into his living room. "Then he got really sick. He almost died. Nobody knows how he survived, but that is how he became a witch."

The table in the living room was covered with bottles of wine and plates of cake. Bowls overflowed with grapes and cherries. From the Soviet-style wooden furniture, different faces stared back at me. Buddha. Krishna. Sai Baba.

Toomas served us plates of oven-baked salmon and potatoes and filled our glasses with sweet red wine. I easily emptied the glass, and he just as quickly refilled it. "Watch how much you drink," Epp said. "He'll just keep refilling it if you keep drinking."

Toomas and Epp spoke to each other and quickly the conversation drifted into linguistic territory that was beyond the means of a beginner.

"Do you speak English at all?" I asked him.

"No," he replied. Then he resumed his dialog with Epp. The words seemed unfamiliar. I guess they were talking about the Other Side. That was the purpose of the visit. I kept drinking wine and eating, moving from the fish to the grapes and then to the cake.

"He has a good appetite," Toomas remarked. I relaxed in my chair and helped myself to some more wine. Toomas pulled out a remote control and turned on the radio, where a choir sang dreamy repetitive verses, probably about the Buddha or Krishna.

This is really ridiculous, I thought as I watched Epp and Toomas converse about the spiritual world. Why do people even believe this junk? Toomas had a chart with a diagram of a human body. He also had a metallic rod in his hands (a magic wand?) that he used to describe to Epp all the routes that positive energy could take.

Epp told Toomas about our upcoming marriage and asked his opinion on the date, but he said he wasn't an expert on numerology.

"You should talk to Anna," he said. "Let me find her number."

Toomas located his appointment book and dialed. Then he switched into Russian. "*Yenich yenech. Yenoozhna nozh,*" he told Anna over the phone. He handed the receiver to Epp.

Epp crouched on the floor and told Anna our story in Russian. How did she know this language so well? I had learned Spanish for years in school, but had lost most of it. I studied Danish for a semester but had lost most of that, too. I had gotten A-s in Latin class, but that was mostly useless.

"Anna says that May is a bad month to get married," Epp reported. "The planets are not aligned to our advantage. She says that June is much better."

"Ok," I mumbled. June sounded better anyway. Maybe I'd find a way to convince my folks it was in my best interests to get married by then. I took another slug of the wine. I was pretty tipsy now. "Toomas, you speak Russian?" I asked.

"A bit better than English," he nodded.

"Do you know any other languages?"

"I know some Finnish and little German, but I am fluent especially in languages that have no names."

Epp spoke awhile longer with Anna the Russian witch, said *'spasibo''* and hung up. Toomas meantime pulled four smooth stones out of a burgundy cloth bag and strapped some kind of metallic device to his wrist. It looked as if he was waiting for an eagle to land on his forearm.

"The energy he commands is very powerful," said Epp. "He needs to protect himself."

Toomas sat down and took a metal pendulum out of the bag. He held the pendulum in one hand and began to ask it questions. When he said Epp's name, the pendulum swung in a tight circular motion. But when he mentioned my name, it began to rotate almost violently in odd directions. I watched his wrist to see if he was controlling this show. I noticed no sudden movements.

"This is really strange," Toomas said, as the pendulum jerked wildly in the air. "You must have come in contact with some really bad energy."

I was unsurprised. I had done my share of bad things, but I had a longstanding feeling that, at some point in time, done something really bad. When I was young, I had called in to a

---

* 'Thanks' in Russian.

psychic hotline advertised on TV to find out who I had been in a previous life. I was expecting Hitler, but was relieved to find out that I had been George Washington.

"Can you fix it?" I asked Toomas.

"I'll manage. You know, a lot of ladies don't want their men fixed completely. They are afraid that if their men have too much esteem, they might leave them, but I think you require special attention."

Toomas put the pendulum down and handed us the stones. "I want you to hold one in each hand, close your eyes and relax." I did as I was told, but snuck a peek of what was going on when I thought nobody was looking.

Toomas dimmed the room lights, turned down the volume of the stereo. I tried to remain alert, but between the wine and the music, I floated into semi-consciousness. I opened my eyes just once more and saw Toomas waving his sparkling magic wand. It almost seemed to spark each time he forced it into the air. Then I closed them, and dozed off into the Estonian Other Side, where there was no bad energy or ugly history and everyone was naturally on time.

Toomas turned on the lights. Epp and I opened our eyes. It took a second to adjust to the brightness. I looked to Epp and she looked at me and we both began to laugh. It was almost uncontrollable. My sides ached as I sat up from my comfortable position on Toomas' couch. Finally, I managed to suppress the sudden case of the giggles. I figured that this is how Toomas must feel inside all the time.

It was late. From Toomas' window, one could see part of the Tartu skyline. Tiny points of line shone everywhere. Small people were doing small things unaware of the winds of energy blowing by.

Toomas poured me a final glass of wine and spoke to Epp, who translated. "He says he did an extra good job to repair your energy levels. After this, your energy levels will be so strong that you won't need them restored for months," she said. "It's very important each day to relax, though, and let the positive energy flow in."

"How did he do that?"

"He's a witch. That's how."

Because we were tipsy, Toomas decided to give us ride home. He took the elevator down with us, and walked us to his car, a cherry-red convertible. Toomas put the keys in the ignition and the speakers popped to the rhythms of the 1950s. It was "Not Fade Away" by Buddy Holly and the Crickets. I would recognize the voice anywhere.

"You like Buddy Holly?" I asked.

"I love rock 'n' roll," Toomas beamed. He put his foot on the gas and we sped away towards the city center, the engine growling all the way. Epp and I snuggled in the back of the convertible in the warm April. The wind blew through the back of our hair. We were like teenage sweethearts.

"I haven't felt this good since I was 15," I told Epp.

"I told you it would be special," she cooed.

"I don't know if he really is a witch or not, but he did something right."

"Toomas said your energy was in all the wrong places," Epp grinned. "He said your conscience was stuck somewhere in your crotch. He put it back where it belongs."

"What's wrong with having your conscience in your crotch?" I joked.

I kissed Epp's cheek as the car sped past the Atlantis Restaurant, its haunting neon lights reflected in the pulsing dark waters of the Emajõgi.

I LIVE
HERE

One thing I love about Tallinn is the cool air. The air rolls in off the Gulf of Finland and floods every street with morning clarity.

I needed the security of the northern air because even though I had grasped the logic behind my marriage to Epp, and I had furnished the emotions, I still had no idea what exactly it meant to be married.

On a Sunday morning I set off from our Kentmanni Street apartment on a walk through the Old Town. It was my first day as an illegal in Estonia. The night before I had kept one eye on the apartment door, waiting for the police to break down the door and banish me from this land. But they never came and I was no longer seriously worried about deportation. I was back to my dependable existential crises.

Who could control his own fate? It seemed impossible. We were but action figures manhandled by the gods. The gods must have washed me up on the Estonian shores for a reason.

This was the door they had opened for me. The only thing left to do was walk through it.

But why did I feel so confused? That's why I needed to walk. If I returned to the streets where I fell in love, I could recapture some of the adventurous spirit that had brought me here. Maybe I could set my world in order and even find the courage to tell my father and mother that I was going to get married.

"Lots of Estonians get married when they are young. It's nothing to be afraid of. I first got married when I was 20," Epp told me the previous evening in bed.

"I know." It wasn't very encouraging to hear it from her lips, because we both knew that her first marriage had ended in divorce. But I didn't want to argue about this topic.

"So why are you being such a coward? Just tell them."

"I will!" Her words burned me. "When I feel like it."

"When will you feel like it?"

"I don't know."

Epp's world was free of fear. When I looked into myself, though, fear is what I found. There was fear of criticism of my choices, fear of rejection of that which was important to me. I had so much fear though I wasn't even sure what it was exactly that terrified me.

❀ ❀ ❀

I stepped out of our building, armed with a digital camera and a journal, a little artistic therapy to help me channel my cowardice. Maybe if I bled it all out into my diary and some inspired shots of Tallinn's Old Town, some hidden strength would surface.

I was walking down the gray street towards the medieval center, when a voice interrupted the morning silence.

"You over there, come here now."

An imposing man in a navy blue security uniform pointed to me from the door of the American embassy.

"Huh?" I turned and walked in his direction.

"Show me your camera," he demanded in accented English.

"What?"

"You are not allowed to take photos of the embassy."

I approached the security guard. It wasn't the first run in I had had with such people. When I was in college in Washington my roommate decided to make a music video. He dressed up like a monkey and I brought the video camera so we could record him clinging to the gates of the White House and going bananas. It was our attempt at art.

The heavily armed White House security personnel were not amused. They let us off without confiscating our video, but the sight of their big guns and the idea that they could technically shoot us with a perfectly reasonable excuse – *Who knew that guy in the monkey suit wasn't a terrorist?* – left me numb with fear for at least 5 minutes.

Now I was in trouble again, not to mention being illegally in a foreign country.

"I didn't take any photos," I told the embassy guard.

"Show me."

I turned the camera on and clicked to the last photo – a shot of Simona pouting in Tartu's Supilinn. I thought it was a cute photo. The security guard showed no emotion.

"Are you sure that's the last photo?"

"See for yourself." I handed him the bulky camera and he flicked through its archive of shots. I hadn't deleted any for months.

"What's this?" He showed me the shots of the protest in front the embassy from several weeks before.

"I took those for the newspaper. I am a journalist."

"Journalist?" He wrinkled his nose as if I was a dirty diaper.

"Yeah. I have written articles for the *Baltic Times*."

The security guard handed me my camera back. "You can go on your way now," he said. "But remember not to take photos of the embassy."

I walked on past the metal posts that blocked off this section of Kentmanni Street. They could be remotely raised or lowered to allow vehicles access to the embassy. It had been like this since I moved in. On State Department orders the embassy had the block closed after the September 11 attacks. The fear was that some would-be suicide bombers would jet in with British stag party goers from London and shatter Tallinn's idyll with a truck full of explosives.

The Estonians swallowed the closure of one of their central streets with the hope that it would one day be reopened. But now the State Department had mandated the erection of a security building in the middle of the street to screen visitors prior to entering the building.

The Americans couldn't move to a roomier location elsewhere in the city. This was the same building where the American legation was housed in the prewar period. It had sentimental value.

I didn't mind the idea. There was no traffic, just 24-hour surveillance in front of our house. Other Kentmanni Street residents were less enthused

"What do they think? That they can just do whatever they want? That we are a bunch of South Africans?" A particularly annoyed resident raged on the evening TV news. "I'm no South African. I am Estonian, and I don't have to take it."

It was kind of arrogant to commandeer a whole block in a foreign city. At the same time, after the bombings in Kenya and Tanzania, their security concerns – our concerns, too – were legitimate. There were people in the world whose main objective was to kill Americans.

I kept my digital camera out of sight until I exited the fiefdom of the embassy security guards. I checked over my shoulder to see if the security guard was still watching me (he was) and I set off towards the spires of St. Nicholas and St. Olaf's Churches.

My mother married for the first time when she was 23. I found the old wedding album one day when I was rummaging through a closet in my parents' house. I was already a teenager then, and I was surprised that I had never seen it before.

My brother was born the year after she married. Mom, her first husband, and my brother all looked happy in the photos, but she and husband number one separated 18 months after that, though the divorce was finalized years later.

One explanation for Mom's failed first marriage was that the two of them were simply too young. Young people were immature. They needed time to find themselves, to spend years, maybe decades, searching their souls for their inner me.

Once they located that special inner self, people could finally settle down, according to this line of thinking. If you looked at Epp's life path, one could say my mother had a point.

But where did that leave me? I was 23. The same age Mom had been when she was first wed, and the same age when Epp separated from her husband number one, because she also had to do some soul searching

I passed by the Nu Nordik design shop and Café Moskva on Freedom Square. I had known Tallinn for less than a year and already felt intimately acquainted with its shops and sights. I rarely went in them though. I usually passed my free time at the bookshop studying Estonian history.

Old ladies with headscarves headed for the Russian Orthodox Church on Toompea passed by as I climbed the hill overlooking the square to get a view of the city. This was where Epp and I ate pizza and spoke of Misha, the bear mascot of the 1980 Olympics. It might have been where I had subconsciously decided on my mate.

I remembered other parts of our August conversation. Epp had attended the Estonian Song and Dance Festival in the mid 1980s. She and her mother wore national costumes and walked from this square to the Song Festival Grounds on Tallinn Harbor with thousands of other Estonians, singing, "*Saa vabaks, Eesti meri*!"

---

*   'Get free, Estonian sea!' in Estonian.

"We all began to cry," she told me. "I didn't even know then that we weren't free, but I could feel it."

It was a romantic image, but the pangs of vulnerability I suddenly felt made me angry. How could anybody look negatively on Epp and me? How could our marriage be such a sin that I couldn't tell anybody about it? I had found a person I wanted to marry and I was young. Wasn't that luck?

Marriages where I came from didn't seem to derive from luck. They were laid out months, even years in advance. Marriages followed years of courtship and were secured by successful career paths. There had to be bachelor parties and bridal showers and rehearsals. The whole affair would cost thousands upon thousands of dollars and rely on a cast of hundreds – the priest, the band, the distant cousins flying in from the West Coast. Anything less was not really a marriage.

I sat down to meditate on this clash of values opposite a metal fence that bore a hand-painted sign – *Baghdad: the Demo Version.* Signs of ongoing construction work stood still beside an unearthed complex of stone foundations in the shadow of St. Nicholas Church.

Buildings had stood in this spot for perhaps centuries until a Soviet bombing raid in March 1944. More than 700 people were killed, 25,000 were left homeless. The fabled Kuld Lõvi hotel once stood on these grounds. From its rooms, Estonian and White Army military commanders had plotted their victory against the Bolsheviks in the Estonian War of Independence in 1919. After March 1944, it was no more.

"Blah blah blah blah?" A young fair-haired man approached me. I couldn't figure out what he was saying until the nasal blend of consonants gave away his mother tongue: Russian.

I tried to remember some of the Russian phrases Ivan had taught me in the office. What was that really important one, the one that had taken 10 attempts to get right?

"*Ya ne ponimayu.* *Ma ei saa aru!*""

"Oh, you speak Estonian," the young man slurred. The top button of his shirt was open and one of his shoelaces was undone. It must have been one rough Saturday night.

"Yes."

"I need to go home," he said in a heavy accent, in Estonian. "I live in Maardu. It's a town not far from Tallinn."

"Maardu?"

"Yes," he paused. Then he slipped back into Russian. I tried to pick meanings out of the soup of Russian sounds, but nothing made sense.

"*Ya ne ponimayu.*"

The Maardu kid scratched his head. He seemed frustrated. "I need 20 kroons," he told me now in English. "I need to take the bus home."

"So you want me to give you money so you can go home to Maardu?"

The Maardu kid suddenly grinned. "Yes," he tossed his head back, like a sea lion catching a fish. "Give me money."

I looked around to see if there was anybody else on whom I could dump my Maardu dilemma, but we were alone.

"Let me think about it."

---

* 'I cannot understand' in Russian.
** 'I cannot understand' in Estonian.

If I gave him the money, I was certain that I would feel like a sucker for at least the next half hour. I didn't give guys money in DC or New York. You could go broke filling up all the empty hands on the sidewalk. At the same time, if I didn't give him the money, I could invite some bad karma into my life. 20 kroons was worth little more than two chocolates. I could spare it.

I fished two bills out of my wallet and handed it to the Maardu kid. He bowed graciously.

"*Spasibo**," he said, and continued in English: "Thank you."

I thought I would feel cheated after handing over my money to the Maardu kid, but a moment later I forgot all about it. I had other things to contemplate.

❀ ❀ ❀

I peered in a souvenir shop window near the town hall square. Varieties of t-shirts were on display, many of them with old World War II-era Soviet and German propaganda posters. There were also t-shirts bearing the faces of the famous: Elvis Presley, Che Guevara, Vladimir Putin.

One blue t-shirt caught my eye. It was based on the 1980s videogame Pac-Man. One Pac-Man on the shirt was dressed in a tuxedo. The other – Mrs. Pac-Man – had on a wedding dress. The bride was smiling. The groom frowned. Above Mr. and Mrs. Pac-Man was printed a caption: Game Over.

Epp called Tiina, the clerk who had registered us for marriage, the Monday after we visited Toomas. She found us a date

---

*   'Thanks' in Russian.

that was not in May on Anna the Witch's advice. We would be married on June 6 instead. 6-6-03. Epp called Anna the witch back to confirm it. Supposedly, it was a good date. I felt bad for all those people who married in May.

What did this mean for my legal status? Apparently nothing. Epp also had called to the Migration Board and cautiously related our tale. In the end, the person on the other end of the phone only wanted to know one thing.

"What nationality?"

"He's American."

"We'll have to see what we can do. But I recommend that you apply for a living permit following the marriage."

The Estonian state might look the other way at my month and a half of illegal presence. It was just some kind of waiting room between the status of a tourist and a resident. That is if they even granted that living permit.

"I wonder what would happen if I had said you were a Russian or Ukrainian citizen," Epp confided in me later. "Do you think they would have been so lenient?"

"I don't know. But that deportation center was definitely designed to hold more people than Giovanni the car burner."

The morning sun warmed town hall square and I tried from every angle to get a good shot of the growing flocks of tourists and pigeons. I looked at a few of my attempts, but none of them pleased me. This is just stupid, I gave up. You can't take a photo of the Old Town. You can only walk through it.

It didn't stop the crowds of travelers from trying the same thing. They walked the square cameras in hand, trying to capture it all on film so they could show it to disinterested family members at home. It was almost as if they preferred to look at Tallinn through a lens rather than with their own eyes.

My ears honed in on the conversations of the tourists. Judging on the languages I heard, the cruise ships had dumped hordes of Italians and Americans on the Estonian capital today. The Italians were better dressed, louder than Estonians, and at least one little fat boy was interrupting the Sunday silence by begging his father for gelato.

The Americans, though, were even louder. You could tell them by their fanny packs nestled above their overflowing waistlines. They also had tour guides to show them the way.

Who could ever really know all there was to know about this city's history? Every loose cobblestone had a story. This is the tree where Peter the Great passed out drunk, I imagined the tour guides saying. And this is the latrine where Swedish King Karl XII relieved himself.

I distracted myself with these thoughts, but Epp's word – "coward" – haunted me. It hurt because it was true. I knew she was right about me. I was soft. It's as my boss in construction had said one day when I hesitated to do something dangerous. "What are you, Justin, some kind of pussy?"

Pussy. Coward. That's what I was. I effeminately scribbled my thoughts in my journal, holding it up against the wall on the House of Black Heads, the carved portrait of Saint Mauritius above its door looking down with pity on the pussy below.

The air is cooler here in the shady streets of the Old City, I wrote in the leather-bound book. *Wouldn't it be great to follow*

it out into the numbing gulf waters, backstroke out past Nais-
saar, and sink into the abyss? No worries. No fear.

"Excuse me, sir, do you speak English?

I spun around and saw a man and a woman. I could tell instantly from their accent that they were Americans. I felt em
barrassed that they had caught me mid-sentence, leaning up
against the House of Black Heads, part poet, part coward.

"Yes, I do."

"Great, do you know where we could find an ATM?"

"Sure, just take the street down and there's a cash machine
on your right."

"Hey, you sound like an American," the man smiled. He
wore a flannel shirt tucked into blue jeans, white sneakers and a
leather jacket. His portly wife had on a white sweater and jeans.
A digital camera hung round her neck like a medallion, swing-
ing just shy of her fanny pack.

"My name is Chip and this is my wife Jeannie," the American said. "We're from Wisconsin. We just got here on Friday.
We're staying at the Vana Wiru hotel." The he pronounced the
'W' in 'Vana Wiru' just like 'Wisconsin', not the sharp way Estonians say it.

"Uh huh." Something inside me recoiled. Why were these
Americans so friendly? As if I cared in what hotel he stayed.

"Where are you from?" said Chip. He touched my arm as
if we were old friends. Other than the odd handshake, nobody
except for Epp had touched me for months.

"New York."

"New Yawk? You don't have one of those funny accents,"
said Chip. "How come?"

I shrugged.

"In what hotel are you staying?" asked Jeannie. She took a step closer and I inched back into the gaze of St. Mauritius.

"I'm not staying in a hotel," I said.

"So you must have come in on a boat," Chip deduced.

"What ship are you on?" asked Jeannie.

"No. I live here."

"Live here?" Chip cried out. "Jeannie, this kid actually lives here!"

"Gee, how does your Ma feel about that one?" Jeannie said. "You sure are a long way from home. What are you doing here?"

"My girlfriend is Estonian."

Chip put his hand on my shoulder. "Congratulations, kid," he gave it a tight, manly squeeze. "You are one lucky son of a gun. You are living the life. Let me take your picture. Jeannie, go on and stand next to him."

Jeannie's perm came up to my shoulder. She put her arm around my back. I smiled for Chip and I understood I was a tale for him to relate to his friends back in Wisconsin. The Americans thanked me and headed off towards the cash machine.

Then I noticed something. I was smiling again. What was it? Maybe it was their boisterous American personalities? Or maybe it was how Chip told me I was "living the life?" I mean, he paid a lot of money to do what I could do any day of the week. I didn't even have to take photos of the Old Town. I walked through it almost every day.

"I live here," I repeated the words.

I picked up my journal again and tried to think about all my problems. How would I deal with my parents, my straying from middle class New York values? What did my impending marriage mean for me? I tried to write, but I just couldn't concentrate. Instead I decided to walk on and enjoy the Old Town. That's what American tourists are supposed to do.

MOTHER'S
DAY

---

*Travelling gets you high like any drug. You become
disoriented. You lose control. And when you adjust to
your new surroundings, you feel that you have learned
something valuable about yourself.*

Before I met Epp, I already had the first half of this decade
planned. Taking breaks of three or four months to raise more
cash doing construction work, I believed I could stay away from
the United States for as long as possible.

First, I would explore the calm forests of northern Europe,
followed by the sun-kissed coastlines of the Mediterranean.
From there, I would enjoy perhaps an interlude on the glaciers
of Greenland before jetting down to Brazil for my backpacker's
victory lap of Rio de Janeiro, Montevideo, Buenos Aires, and,
finally, Santiago – the capital of Chile.

According to those travel plans, I was supposed to reach
the Chilean coast by sometime in 2006. Finland's Foreign Correspondents Program obviously altered my itinerary, but not
my ambition.

These days I sat in an Internet Café in Tallinn exchanging e-mails with a school in Valparaíso, Chile, that might offer us jobs teaching English. Epp encouraged it. South America was also on her list of places to see.

"We can live like bohemians. You can get a certificate so that you can teach English, and I can offer private lessons," she said one night during a commercial break for *The Bold and the Beautiful*. "We could have a little apartment on the sea, buy fresh fruit from the market, and eat our breakfast watching the sunrise," she dreamed.

"I'm not the first Petrone to pass through South America," I said. "My grandfather's grandfather Gennaro worked in Buenos Aires before he moved to New York."

"So you have South American roots? Maybe you have cousins there we could visit."

"Not that I know of, but I think I have some cousins in Italy."

"We can visit them first," Epp was excited. "And then get a last minute deal to Chile."

Epp loved the idea of last minute deals. She had friends that circled the globe on budget airlines taking unusual routes to popular destinations. Flying direct to Seoul was too expensive for bohemians. But flying from Tallinn to Frankfurt to Johannesburg to Kuala Lumpur to Tokyo and finally on to Seoul? That just might be an affordable last minute deal.

My attention wandered to the TV. An attractive woman was standing in downtown traffic in a European city. She pulled her t-shirt off, revealing her naked chest. A nearby fire hydrant exploded simultaneously, soaking the bare-breasted European, who arched her neck in ecstasy. It was a commercial for soap and one of my favorites.

"I can't believe they showed that on TV," I said.

"What?"

"They would never show you that in the US."

"Why not?"

"Boobs are too risqué for some Americans."

They weren't too risqué for me. I liked Europe's liberal attitudes. When I was 14, my mother and father and I visited Zurich. Our business-class hotel was next to an adult movie theater. Swiss kids, no older than me, guzzled beers in picturesque lanes and handed out flyers to peep shows. I was very impressed.

"Look, I'm sorry," I felt some need to apologize for noticing the nude soap commercial. "It must be a full moon or something."

The moon had been causing trouble. People seemed more emotional. I had seen more couples bickering than usual in the Old Town. Some of them were even Estonians. Estonian lovers' quarrels usually didn't wind up with broken glass and bashed fruit, though. They were more like heated legal debates. A mutual inquest into how highly organized plans had gone awry.

One night after going to Epp's office, the moon got to me, too.

We had spoken to my parents earlier in the day, but I still hadn't found the strength to tell them.

"So, how are things?" my father had asked.

"Things are, well, you know, they're fine. Just fine," I told him.

"Why don't you just say, 'Mom, Dad, I have good news, Epp and I are going to be married,'" Epp said on the walk home. "That's all it takes. I am getting pretty sick of pretending like nothing is going on."

"I don't feel like ruining my night."

"You are being selfish. Think about how I feel. Think about how they would feel if they knew. Don't be such a coward."

"I am not a coward."

"Well you are acting like one."

"I am not a coward!" I screamed for all to hear. I was so consumed by anger, that I pulled off my work bag and threw it at a building in frustration.

"Why did you throw your bag?" Epp stepped away from the beast that just a moment before was her boyfriend.

"I don't know," I tried to calm myself and pulled the bag out a puddle. The strap was broken. "I'm sorry," I was ashamed. "I just feel on edge today."

We were walking home after meeting with Piret, an Estonian girl who had lived in Greenland. Epp had poured tea and hit up Piret for travel tips.

Going to Greenland was a travel plan I had brought to the relationship. I was into fjords, she was into ashrams. We decided that life was long. We could do both. Epp would apply to the Nordic Council for funding to write articles about Greenlandic life. I would come as her photographer and personal assistant. We would take Air Greenland to Nuuk to relish a new traveling high and spread the gospel of the Nordic way to Estonian readers.

"I'm sorry I lost my temper," I said.

"It's ok," she said. "One day I will tell our children that their father was once so mad he threw his bag against a wall."

"Why would you say that?"

"I think they'd be very impressed. Come on, let's go home," Epp said. "I bought curd cheese today. I am going to make a cake."

We linked arms. We were friends again.

That was our life. Just as quickly as we argued, we made up. And our feet may have been on Maakri Street in Tallinn, but our minds were floating somewhere between the South Pacific and the Greenland Sea.

❋ ❋ ❋

It was May, and Tallinn buzzed with Australians, Swedes, Finns, Brits, Americans, and Japanese tourists. They were everywhere I went, and they were speaking to everyone in English. For some reason, this bothered me. Why couldn't they just buy a guidebook and at least try to speak some Estonian?

I tried to stay clear of the hordes of travelers and carry on with my business. They were on holiday. I lived here.

Epp didn't feel well. Something was not right. For several mornings she couldn't get out of bed. She was just too sleepy, she explained. Instead I was the one who made the coffee, turned on the radio, and helped my lazy spouse start the day.

"Five more minutes," she would say, stretching her arms after finishing her morning coffee. "Let me sleep until the caffeine hits my blood."

Later Epp told me she was sick. She sent me to the nearby pharmacy to buy some medicines and wrote down them down on a piece of paper. *Islandi samblik. Pärnaõietee. Vaarikavarretee*. *Hematogeen.*

I knew Epp couldn't live without her life-sustaining blood candy bars, *hematogeens*, but what were those other three?

"They are teas. Just ask the clerk. I feel so sleepy," she yawned.

The pharmacy around the corner was distinguished by its inclusion in a neighborhood of florists, hair salons, and two sex shops. When I entered the pharmacy, the clerk came out of a back room, where I am sure she had been busy counting pills or reading a a celebrity magazine. She was an ancient woman with a gray ponytail. I knew her face. I had been here a few times.

"Yes?" she asked. She looked in my direction, staring blankly, as if I was a bottle of cough syrup or tube of cortisone cream.

"I need *Islandi samblik, pärnaõietee*, and some *vaarikavarretee*," I stumbled over the words' tricky vowels.

"*Islandi samblik, vaarikavarretee*, and what was the last one?" She seemed irritated, as if I was keeping her from doing something more important.

"*Pärnaõietee.*"

"What?"

"*Pärnaõietee.*"

---

*   'Icelandic moss,' 'linden blossom tea,' and 'raspberry stalk tea' in Estonian.

"Oh, *p ä r n a õ i e t e e*," she said.

"That's right. *Pärnaõõõõietee*," I imitated her. I had gotten better at making the 'õ' sound, but I wasn't a master yet. You just gave your regular 'o' a little squeeze, I hypothesized.

The clerk pulled out three bags of what appeared to be dried moss with some twigs and leaves mixed in. This couldn't be the medicine Epp had requested. I felt as if we were doing a drug deal. Did she grow this stuff at home?

"Is that everything?"

"No, I need some *hematogeens*."

"How many?"

"Four," I said. I knew how much Epp loved these blood bars. "Make that five."

The clerk rang me up. I put the money in the clinical plastic dish, where a moment later she deposited my change.

"Sorry if you had any problems understanding me," I said. "Estonian is not my native language."

"You speak very well," she was robotic. She turned mechanically and walked into the back room of the *apteek*.

Epp drank the mossy teas that night, but she still felt tired. She also said her back ached. Something was different about her, but what? Maybe there was some astrological or numerological explanation for all of this.

I went to the *Baltic Times* office, made my phone calls, wrote up a news article for Ivan – he got to write about politics and foreign policy, I got to write about new shopping centers and ferry routes – and went home to have lunch with Epp and see if she felt any better.

It was a warm, breezy day in early May. The fragrant trees of Tallinn had started to blossom. Narcotic-like pollen clogged the air. For the first time since we moved in to our Kentmanni apartment, I could see from the street that all the windows to our quarters were open. White curtains fluttered inside and out.

In the apartment, Epp reclined on the bed. She was eating a pear and reading a book about the tumultuous romance of John Lennon and Yoko Ono.

"Do you feel any better?" I asked her.

"A bit," she fidgeted with her hands. "There's something I have to tell you."

"What?" I leaned in closer.

She reached behind her back and pulled out a small, plastic white tube. "You made me pregnant."

I sat down on the bed.

"We are going to have a baby," Epp wiped a tear from her eye. "I already figured it out. It will be born in early January. So a little Capricorn!"

"A little Capricorn?" I was numb. I stood up from the bed and walked into the kitchen.

"What's wrong?" Epp asked.

I lay down on our kitchen floor. It was barely big enough to host my body. My feet lay near the half-functional stove, my head an inch away from the antique radiator. I tried to think, but all I could feel was raw pressure on every limb.

"Are you okay?" Epp followed me in. "Do you not want to have this baby? Because if you don't I can raise it myself."

"No, I want to have the baby," I sighed. I felt almost drunk. My ears and lips were hot with blood. My heart motored along in my chest. My arms were too shaky to be used. I tried to focus on the ceiling. I didn't know what to do about my anxious stomach. My gut was bloated with enough gas to fill a zeppelin.

"Oh boy... or girl!" I let out a nervous chuckle. The air passed from my lungs. "This is big."

"Come and lie with me," Epp said. "Please."

"I will. Just let me catch my breath."

"Father." It sounded like something I could never be. Fathers were respected for their wisdom and resourcefulness. They knew how to build houses and repair automobiles. I had little advice to give and no resources. But I was going to be a father. It just was a question of which kind of father I would become.

The first person I told about my impending fatherhood was a complete stranger. We were both drinking beers at Molly Malone's pub on town hall square. After noticing my accent when I ordered, he struck up a conversation. The stranger was an American IT guy in town for business. Two years older than me, he had a three-year-old son. Fatherhood, he explained while sucking on a Saku Originaal, was easy.

"You have to remember something," the stranger said. "Humans have been raising children since they lived in caves. If a caveman could raise a kid, you can too." His words helped answer some of my questions, but I was unconvinced.

"I don't think my folks will take this well," I confided.

"They might be a little shocked. But, in the end, they are getting a grandchild out of the deal. Once they realize this, they will be happy."

"They'll think I am too young."

The stranger laughed and took another gulp of his beer. "You are older than you think you are," he said.

I went into the bank on the way home to pick up some cash. A young man stood near the ATM, while a cute toddler, his child, hopped around the bank screaming "*issi, issi.*"

When you are preparing to be a father, you start to notice two phenomena that you may have ignored previously. One is pregnant ladies, whose bulging bellies seem to lurk behind every corner. The other is children, most of whom you will suddenly find adorable.

"*Issi, issi,*" the cute little girl cried. It meant "Daddy" in Estonian, but to me it had a slightly different connotation. A daddy was older and resourceful. You needed to have a few laugh lines around your eyes and a hammer in your belt to be one of those, so, by definition, it was kind of hard to be a 23-year-old daddy. But an *issi*? An *issi* was a clown, a clumsy giant created solely for entertaining young people.

"*Issi!*" the little girl cried as the man swept his daughter up into his arms and walked out of the bank. The way he did it seemed so natural. He was a guy, just like me, who somewhere had a girlfriend or wife with whom he had conceived a baby that desired attention. He gladly gave it, and for this he was rewarded with affection and a comical title: *issi.*

I didn't know if I would be the best father but I was pretty sure I could manage being an *issi.*

265

When I told Epp this later in our tiny kitchen, she kissed me on the cheek. "It's good you have decided to be an *issi*," she was mixing batter for another cake. "'Daddy' won't work for us anyway. It sounds too much like *tädi*.*"

I decided that the best day to break the news to my parents would be Mother's Day. It was an appropriate day; a day when perhaps the soothing messages of global maternity would overcome rash judgments about the wisdom of a 23-year-old who, a year out of college, had run off to Europe, secretly planned to get married, and now would have a love child to show for it.

Epp and I strolled through the Old Town. We took a dusty underground corridor past a guitar player in an Iron Maiden t-shirt who was singing for vodka money. Moments later we stepped up into the main railroad station called *Balti jaam*.

Balti jaam was a miserable pocket of post-Soviet existence. The first face I saw when I came up the stairs was a staggering woman with bruises on her cheeks cursing at us in Russian. The next was an old Estonian man with a band-aid on his nose, looking for a handout. I gave him nothing and felt no remorse.

I was a person with social democratic tendencies. Conservatives, in my experience, were snobby ideological purists who worshipped at the altars of St. Reagan and St. Thatcher. Social democrats were like Tarja Halonen and Erkki Tuomioja. They

---

*   'Aunt' in Estonian.

didn't just wear jeans to work, they even took saunas together. They were my kind of people.

In places like the *Balti jaam*, though, I became a neoliberal convert. Maybe Mart Laar, Estonia's first elected prime minister since the 1930s, was right. The stench of socialism in places like *Balti jaam* could only be wiped away with extra strength commie cleanser. Privatize this shit hole, I thought to myself. And sell it off to the bloodthirsty capitalists.

We came to *Balti jaam* for the flowers. Though Epp was not yet a mother, by January she would be an *emme* as she was carrying tiny little human being inside of her. She called it her *tita* or "baby", another irresistibly cute name that complimented *issi*. We were all there, to think of it, *emme*, *issi*, and *tita*, buying flowers in celebration of Mother's Day in the spring sunshine.

My phone rang.

"Hi, it's your mother."

My stomach cramped.

"Happy Mother's Day!"

"Thanks. Your brother called me first thing this morning."

"Well, how are you? We were planning to call you later."

"That's what I thought, but, I figured I'd give you a call anyway. Where are you, it sounds like you're outside somewhere?"

"We're in a market buying flowers."

"Flowers?"

"Yes, I..."

"Well, we're just about to head out the door here. We're going to my mother's to have brunch. Aunt Mary is coming. The whole family is going to be there, except you."

"The whole family?" I felt as if I were carrying some kind of nuclear device. Would it be appropriate to nuke my mother on Mother's Day, so she could bring her radioactive self to brunch and contaminate the whole family? Or maybe to put it off longer, so I could nuke both her and my father at a more convenient time? I opted for the latter.

"Mom, you sound really busy. You have a happy Mother's Day and we'll talk later in the week."

She said she loved me and I told her the same. Then we hung up.

"Why didn't you tell her," Epp slammed the flowers down on the counter to pay for them.

"It's not the right time."

"Come on. It's never going to be the right time. Just tell them."

"They are going to a brunch at grandma's house. The whole family is going to be there. Plus I wanted my father to be on the phone, too. We're going to have a baby. They'll find out sooner or later."

"Ah, I guess you are right."

I rubbed my hands through my hair and looked up at Toompea hill.

"Let's not let this ruin our day," she said in the sunlight, her arms full of flowers. "Things are good. Things are not bad."

A week later, I sat down in her office to make the call. The modern wooden Scandinavian office furniture was clinical and somewhat comforting. It reminded me of a doctor's office: a safe place from which to give a patient the bad news.

At precisely 4 pm – 9 am in New York – I picked up the receiver and dialed. I was seasick with anxiety, but I knew it was something that must be done. All I had to do was stop thinking, open my mouth, and let the words out.

The phone rang. My father picked up.

"Hey, Dad, it's me."

"Hi Justin, how are you? I am just downstairs making coffee and watching CNN."

"I'm good, Dad, really good. Is Mom also awake?"

"Hello?" I heard my mother's voice boom through the phone. She must have picked up the receiver in their bedroom.

"Good morning, it's me."

"How are you, honey?" She was happy to hear her son's voice.

"I'm good, very good," I tried to appear as positive as possible. If I could remain positive, I could make to the end of the phone call. "Well, listen, I just wanted to say that I have really good news. You two are going to be grandparents!"

There was a long pause. I heard my father say "you've got to be kidding me" under his breath. Then he said, "Congratulations!"

My mother remained silent. Then she asked, "Well, what are you going to do?"

"Well, Epp hasn't seen the doctor yet, but the baby is due in January and..."

"So I assume you'll be getting married?" my father interrupted.

"Of course," it felt good to tell the truth. "We already picked out a date, June 6."

Both were silent. Maybe they were stunned. "This is good news," my father said. "We've always wanted to be grandparents."

Even though I had finally told them the truth, I was still throbbing with adrenaline. My ears and lips were again hot. I wiped sweat from my brow.

"How long have you known?" my mother asked.

"Well, we were going to tell you last week. But I thought it might be better..."

"If you didn't surprise me before we went to brunch."

"Yeah."

"I had a feeling something was up when you mentioned flowers," she said. "How is Epp feeling?"

"Well, she is right here, if you want to talk to her."

Epp looked pleased that I had finally told them. She took the receiver and said hello.

"Yes, I am feeling fine," she said. "I've just felt a little sleepy."

I gave Epp my seat and she and my mother talked on in the afternoon sunlight. I walked across the room and sat in a chair, looking out the window towards the Old Town. I was proud of myself. A few more moments like these and I might even be fit to be someone's father.

IN THE HEART
OF ESTONIA

"It's me, Indrek. We are waiting for you around the corner."

I pulled on my sweatshirt, grabbed my notebook, and told him I would be there in two minutes.

I had pitched a story to the *Baltic Times* on the Estonian music scene. Who were its stars and why hadn't more of them broken through to the global mainstream? As always, the editors in Riga tried to make it into a 'Baltic' story. Sometimes I felt as if the only place the Baltic States existed was in their heads. But since Indrek managed one Latvian band in addition to his roster of Estonian talent, he was an ideal source.

The convertible was parked in front of the corner grocery. In it sat three men. The lanky one in the driver's seat was checking his watch. The round one in the passenger's seat had red hair, a moustache, and was chatting on his mobile phone. The short one in the backseat wore a black leather jacket and looked dangerous.

"You must be Justin," the redhead waved to me, "get in. I'm Indrek."

I opened the door and sat down next to the little tough guy with the leather jacket. He stared at me, but didn't say a word.

"Justin, this is my brother, Andres," Indrek gestured to the driver while still on the phone. "And this is Urmas from Blind," Indrek said, motioning at the guy next to me.

Urmas looked at me again and said nothing. He didn't have to, because I already knew who he was. Indrek had sent a sample CD of artists he managed to the *Baltic Times* office. Blind was the "most successful Estonian rock band." According to their bio, Blind's ambition was to be "bigger than the Beatles." Urmas, who sang and played guitar in the group, was their Lennon.

"They play in New York all the time. They are even on a New York label," Indrek said as Andres drove the car through Tallinn.

"Listen to this," said Indrek. "It's their new album, *Estonians*."

"Creative title," I said to Urmas.

"Our last record was called *The Breast Off*," he stared at the countryside as we whizzed south. "In New York, there is another group called Blind, so we perform there as the Totally B L I N D Drunk Drivers."

"Good name."

"It was especially good when we rented a van and drove around the US. The guy at the car rental asked, 'Who are you?' – 'We're the Totally B L I N D Drunk Drivers.'"

Indrek popped the CD into the car stereo and drums began to pound followed by rumbling of a bass guitar and heavy power chords. Floating atop the dissonance was Urmas' voice.

The song owed a debt to punk rock, but had a strong melody. Urmas had some Lennon in him after all.

"Who were you talking to before," I asked Indrek.

"That was my wife," he answered.

"Indrek is always talking to his wife," Urmas was deadpan. "He loves her so much."

"I'm getting married soon," I announced to the car. Since Indrek was married, I guessed it might be ok to tell these Estonian guys a bit more about my personal life.

"To an Estonian girl?" asked Indrek. "What's her name?"

"Epp."

"I once had a girlfriend named Epp," Urmas said.

"Don't tell me you are marrying one of Urmas' ex-girlfriends," Indrek chuckled.

I was pretty sure I knew all the names of Epp's ex-boyfriends, and I didn't recall ever hearing about an Urmas. At the same time, she *was* older than me. Maybe she had forgotten to tell me about one or two or three of them.

"Was your Epp from Viljandi County?" I asked Urmas.

He paused a second, to relish the awkwardness of the moment. "No. My Epp was from Paide."

"That's where we are going," said Indrek. "You know, lots of Estonian musicians are from Paide."

"Like who?"

"Like the famous composer Arvo Pärt. Most of the band Ruffus is from around there too," said Indrek.

"Are you from Paide?" I asked Urmas.

"No. I'm just another guy from Tallinn. Do you know what they call Paide?"

"No."

"The heart of Estonia. It's because it's in the heart of Estonia."

Urmas kept his straight face for a moment and then cracked a smile. For the first time since I got in the car, I laughed. Maybe Urmas wasn't so mysterious after all. He was just a rocker. He had to look tough to hide his sensitive soul.

Ruffus was the new name of Vaiko Eplik's rock band. The 21-year-old singer rechristened Claire's Birthday in the run-up to their performance at the Eurovision Song Contest in Riga. All spring long, it was impossible to escape their song, "Eighties Coming Back". I heard it in cafes, at the supermarket, and in cabs.

Epp received free tickets to go see Ruffus play at *Linnahall*. By then, she was already pregnant, sleepy, and experiencing the first pangs of morning sickness. We decided that I would go enjoy Ruffus alone.

Linnahall looked like an ancient Aztec fortress constructed for worship and sacrifice. Built in 1980 for the Olympic Games, it was originally called the V. I. Lenin Palace of Culture and Sport which, when you consider the links to paternalistic deities and ritualistic killing, kind of made sense.

There were other acts performing that afternoon at the *Linnahall* besides Ruffus. Finally Vaiko came out with his guitar. He plugged it into his amp, the guys in the band all looked at one another, and they swung into "Eighties Coming Back". The crowd remained seated and clapped politely, looking some-what pleased. This was Estonia's song. They had to support it.

Listening to Vaiko sing, I was impressed. I had tried to write songs, but none were as catchy as his. I couldn't believe he was younger than me.

I decided that such musical talent was not only acquired. Sometimes it just manifested itself. You give a kid a guitar and, before you know it, they're selling ringtones of his tunes for mobile phones. I knew that day in the *Linnahall* that Vaiko would win Eurovision. He was too talented to lose.

❀ ❀ ❀

On the day of the Eurovision contest, Epp decided to make a cake. I could smell it as the time for the big event neared. Life with Epp could be very sweet. I imagined we could grow old just like that, eating cakes and watching song competitions.

Epp had made more cakes since she became pregnant. She craved other things, too. One was plum juice. Like a dutiful husband-to-be, I brought her one container from the store. She drank that in 10 minutes. Then I brought home two contain-ers. 20 minutes later it was gone. After running through all the plum juice they had at the corner shop, it was time to turn to Stockmann. I bought her six boxes of the pungent purple stuff. I had no desire to drink it. For some reason, though, her juice craving ended after she pounded three more boxes in a row. All of a sudden she said it made her nauseous. We now had had three unopened boxes of the natural diuretic in our fridge for three weeks ready for whenever her craving might return.

I nestled on the couch with my cake, and skimmed through a Eurovision special in a newspaper. The Estonian media treated Eurovision like parliamentary elections. There were columns by thought leaders on the merits of each song and the odds of their favorites winning the contest. ETV, the state television network, showed video clips of the entries from other countries to get the audience familiar with the selections for the big night.

The contest began and Epp joined me in front of our TV. We were betting on Vaiko to carry the evening, but since we couldn't vote for Estonia, we had to settle for other candidates. Who to choose? Most money was running on t.A.T.u., the Russian lesbian pop duo. Ivan told me one day in the office that his little sister Ekaterina would definitely be voting for the lesbians in the short prep-school dresses.

"She listens to them constantly, every day, so I have to listen to t.A.T.u. all the time," he shook his head. "It's so annoying. I think she's in love with them."

Epp and I were split. She preferred the Norwegian entry, a bittersweet piano ballad sung by a towhead with a perfect smile. I preferred the Cypriot singer, who wore a white suit and was supported by a disco beat and slutty backing singers.

Most of the acts had slutty backing singers, actually. A few others tried to win people's votes different ways. An Austrian comedian, for example, was backed by a band of stuffed animals. A Ukrainian sang in Spanish and English. His song title was "Hasta la Vista, Baby."

Towards the end of the show, poor Ruffus trotted into the circus of boob-shaking dancers, pelvis-gyrating male divas, and horrendous haircuts to perform. Up on the Eurovision stage, though, there was little room for actual music. You needed a few back flips, loads of sexual innuendo, and some pyrotechnics to capture anyone's attention.

In the end, Ruffus came in 21st place, right between Cyprus and Portugal. Cyprus got its 12 points from Greece, which later reciprocated.

"They always do that," Epp said. "The countries form gangs that vote for one another."

Epp's Norwegian crooner was number four, backed by strong Scandinavian support – Iceland gave him 12 points. The Russian lesbians and a Belgian act struggled for the top, but in the end some half-naked Turkish harem girls clawed their way to disco victory.

"How can Turkey win? They're barely in Europe!" I protested.

"But Turkey is part of Europe. We share a lot of history," Epp said.

"Ok, but you are never going to convince me that Israel is in Europe. Don't they have a Middle Eastern Song Contest?"

"You've never been to Tel-Aviv. It's very European."

"If Israel and Turkey get to participate, then where's Lebanon?"

"Ok," Epp thought for a moment, "you have a point."

And so, the 2004 contest would be held in Istanbul, my former student Marko, the charismatic and well-dressed TV host, informed us live from Riga. Marko grinned when he announced Turkey's victory – he would get an all-expenses paid trip next year to an exotic country.

What happened to Vaiko afterwards was a different story. I read news reports the following week that he had received death threats from angry Estonians for the poor performance of his song. Sahlene's "Runaway" had come in third the previous year. Dave Benton and Tanel Padar's "Everybody" had won the contest the year before that. But Vaiko's song had come in 21st place, almost last. He had disgraced the good name of Estonia.

One day in a bar, Estonia's angry Eurovision fans caught up with Vaiko. According to newspapers, there had been a scuffle. Vaiko had been hit. Luckily, for the guitarist and composer, none of his fingers had been broken.

That had been just a few days ago.

"Urmas! Indrek!" Dressed in a black sweatshirt, Vaiko approached us in the rows of benches that made up the Paide amphitheater. We had pulled into the tidy city of parks, churches, and impressive castle ruins just minutes before. Indrek and Urmas had already chugged cans of beer. Mine was half drained. Andres drank nothing – he was our designated driver.

They all exchanged pleasantries while I eyed a quartet of blonde chicks in sunglasses a few rows away.

"Who are *they*?" I whispered to Urmas.

"Heh," he wiped the foam from another beer from his mouth. "That's Vanilla Ninja."

Vanilla Ninja? I had eaten ice cream that bore their image. Now they were only two rows away. In America, such stars would have bodyguards and dressing rooms. In Estonia, they hung out with everyone else.

"Nobody can support themselves being a rock musician in Estonia," Urmas said as I took notes for my story. "We all have day jobs. I have a radio show with Indrek. The drummer in our band works in IT."

"Who's this?" asked Vaiko, looking at me. From a distance, Vaiko looked young and photogenic. Up close, the dark-haired rocker was as scruffy and haggard as a street kid from *Oliver Twist*. Maybe the stress of Eurovision had worn him down.

"That's Justin," said Indrek. "He's come to interview you about Estonian rock music."

"Good," Vaiko looked at me, "but if you want to talk, you'll have to walk. I'm hungry."

We walked towards the center of Paide past the castle ruins. According to a sign, it was built in the 13th century by the Livonian Order. Back then, the city was called Weissenstein. I decided it was good that the Germans no longer ran Estonia. The Estonians had much better names for their cities.

"So where are you from?" Vaiko asked. He spoke with a convincing British accent. If he had said he was from Manchester and not Estonia, I might have believed him.

"New York."

"*New York!*" he lit up a cigarette. "That's where my favorite rock groups are from, like the Strokes. Do you know the Strokes?"

"Not personally. But I know of their music."

"You should know it, because it's bloody brilliant."

We walked to a café in an ancient building, perhaps also built by the Order. Inside sat a bored-looking Estonian maiden in medieval garb. We might have been her first customers all day. Without us, she would still be sitting there, maybe waiting for some guy to come and save her.

"Let's order up a round of *pelmeenid** and some drinks," said Vaiko. He was flanked by his band mates from Ruffus. None of them spoke to me. Instead they went upstairs to play pool.

Everyone else was drinking beer, but Vaiko ordered carbonated water instead.

"Don't you want a beer?" I asked him.

"I don't drink anymore," he answered, pulling out his wallet. "I had a wild youth."

"Did you hear that Tanel got married?" Urmas said to Vaiko."

"I read about it in the paper like everyone else," Vaiko answered.

I realized they were talking about Tanel Padar, the singer who won Eurovision with Dave Benton. I had seen him play on TV and read about his marriage in the papers. Vaiko and Urmas were on a first-name basis with the guy. Maybe they were friends. Uncle Tiit was right. Estonia was one big rock and roll high school!

Our order of *pelmeenid* and drinks arrived and we went upstairs. Vaiko sat opposite me in a booth. The interview began.

"It's good to see you are still in one piece. I read you've been in danger after Eurovision."

---

* 'meat dumplings' in Estonian.

Vaiko scowled, "People take Eurovision too seriously. It's bloody stupid. Don't tell me you actually watched it."

"My girlfriend loves it. She even made a cake."

"Indrek's wife loves Eurovision, too," said Urmas.

"We had no idea we would actually be selected to go," said Vaiko, lighting up another smoke. "We're a rock band, like the Strokes. We don't belong in Eurovision. But before we talk about music, we have to talk about the war."

"War?" he caught me off guard.

"It's just not cool what you American cats are doing in Iraq. Just not cool."

I agreed with him, but was also offended. Weren't there Estonian troops there too? Wasn't it our doing, as opposed to my doing?

"I sent my senators letters telling them not to support it. They didn't listen to me."

"Oh, bloody hell." Vaiko slammed his hands on the table. "No country should be able to do that to another country. Look at our history. Do you want to know what the Germans did to my relatives? You don't want to know, it's too bloody disgusting."

I realized that Vaiko was the first Estonian who had ever said anything bad about the Germans to me. All other Estonians spoke about the Soviets. But that three-year period of German occupation also robbed families of their loved ones. I had read that the entire Estonian Jewish community that was left after the Soviet retreat in 1941, about a thousand people, had been arrested within weeks of the Germans' arrival and fewer than a dozen survived. Most countries in Europe had suffered from one aggressor in the Second World War. Estonia was hit from both sides.

"Hopefully the Iraq war will be over soon," I said.

"It will go on for years, just like Vietnam." He took another drag from his cigarette. "Ok, enough about war, let's talk about music."

When it came to music, Vaiko was half idealist, half cynic. His job, he said, was to make the best music possible and get it out there. He had little interest in selling out, which is why he didn't expect Eurovision to carry him far.

"So what, so you get a label somewhere in Europe to put out your stuff and they support you for a little while and then they drop you, then you are back to bloody square one," he said.

"Do you think your name is too ethnic? Is it hard for Estonians to break through because of that?" I asked for my interview.

"I have a terrific name. Vaiko Eplik? It sounds like it's bloody Japanese! It's not about your name. It's about making brilliant music. If it's brilliant, then people will listen, no matter who or where you are."

I listened to Vaiko's lecture as a student. He reminded me of my college roommate, the one who got busted for dressing up like a monkey and hanging on the White House fence for an art project. For real artists, life wasn't about success. It was about the pleasure of creating. Vaiko really didn't care about winning Eurovision. He wanted to write good songs.

After the guys played a few rounds of pool, we carried our drinks out to the courtyard. I was mostly on my own. Everyone spoke in Estonian, and I had been learning for less than a year. I couldn't keep up.

Vaiko took a sip of his water, and I noticed the shiny wedding band on his finger.

"You're married, eh?" I already knew the answer, but it's hard to admit to a person that you've read about them in a newspaper.

"And a father!" he said.

"You know, I am going to be a father soon," I said. I noticed my heart started beating faster when I said it. Even after a few beers, I couldn't withstand the adrenaline rush that came whenever I thought about my future.

"Congrats," Vaiko held out his hand.

"Is it hard?" I asked.

"Yes and no."

"But how is your life different?"

"It changes you, man. It's like they say, child is father of the man. Before my son was born, I used to walk down the street and not look at anybody. I was so scared about what other people thought of me. But now, I hold my head up high. I don't care what those wankers think."

"So it's not so tough?"

"Well, living with a baby is definitely tough. The little bugger cried all night long for months. You'll go out of your mind putting up with it. But it gets better. I can't wait 'til he turns three."

"Why three?"

"Because then he'll be his own little person. He can walk and talk. Then we can get him started on guitar."

I stood there taking notes on fatherhood from a 21-year-old rock star. He had already set up camp atop a mountain I had yet to climb. But if he could do it, even with all his talent, I decided there was a good chance I could make it to the top as well.

Later Vaiko and the band played a set in front of the packed amphitheater.

"I get upset, I get upset," Vaiko sang over melancholic guitars and keyboards. He turned the phrase over and over through the microphone and I envied the way he was able to express simple thoughts in a direct way. If I had been up there, I would have spent three paragraphs' worth of words trying to express the same feeling. I still had a long journey ahead of me as an aspiring artist, not to mention husband and father-to-be.

Ruffus' melodies put me in a blue mood. When Vanilla Ninja came on stage, that all changed. They had a light show, dance moves, big beats, and attractive singers. The little girls in the audience looked very happy. I felt better, too. I didn't care if they were just a pop group with their own ice cream. I liked the Ninja's attitude.

"They're not bad," I slurred to Urmas.

"Let's go up there," he raised a fist.

"Where?"

"On stage. The next one is 'Klub Kung Fu.' Let's go."

"But we can't go up there."

Urmas and the others were already headed to the back of the stage. With beer in hand, I followed them and we climbed the steps. From up here, the crowd was barely visible. All you could see were the hot spotlights. No wonder the Ninjas wore shades.

The next song came on and the Ninjas began to chop their way through their greatest hit. We stood in the back, jumping up and down in the lights and singing along with a crowd that gathered on stage.

"This is surreal," I told Urmas.

"Just enjoy it," he said and chopped his arm in the air.

Andres pulled the convertible into a gas station and Indrek hopped out. We were about half an hour out of Paide and the spring sky was dark, save a streak of light that hovered on the horizon.

"Just getting more beer," Indrek said.

"More beer? But we already drank," I tried to count, "a lot of beer."

"There's always room for more beer," said Urmas.

"Well how many beers can one drink?"

"I don't know. That's what I keep trying to find out."

Indrek returned with two six packs, ripped one open, and distributed the goods. We all drank up, except for Andres. He was sober and grooving to the new Blind album again. I wasn't ready to stop the party anyway. It was the first time I had been out having fun since I moved to Tallinn.

About 20 minutes and two beers passed before my lower body came under unbearable pressure. I didn't want to inconvenience anybody, though. Maybe I could hold it until we got to Tallinn.

"Andres, pull the car over," Indrek grumbled. "I've got to take a leak."

"Me, too," I said. I was glad to know Indrek and I were on the same schedule.

Andres pulled the car over on a deserted stretch of the Tallinn-Tartu highway. There were no inviting bushes or trees anywhere, just fields. Somewhere in the distance, I heard a cow moo. Indrek, Urmas, and I lined up along side one another and did our business.

"It's good to be men," Indrek said. "The world is our toilet."

Just then, my phone rang. It was Epp.

"Where are you? It's almost 3 am," she said.

"I'm sorry I didn't call earlier, honey," I slurred. "I've just been doing some really interesting interviews."

"I am here in bed and I feel so nauseous. Are you still in Paide?"

"No. I am peeing in a field with a bunch of Estonian rock stars."

"Sounds like fun," she laughed. "It's good to know you finally made some friends."

SASS

"Where are you going?" I asked her. — "To buy my grandfather some sugar-free candy," she answered. "Papa is a diabetic, but he loves candy, I always try to buy some when I go to visit him."

Our Estonian life was like a game of pinball. We bounced back and forth between three locations: Tallinn, Tartu, and Viljandi County.

I longed to go to Pärnu or Kuressaare on west coast of Estonia, some place with a beach. But here we were again in the middle of South Estonia, in Viljandi in a supermarket buying sugar-free candy for Epp's grandfather, Karl.

Epp called him Papa. She loved him more than I could remember loving any of my older relatives. Papa was a pensioner. He had been a veterinarian before he retired. When Epp was a child, she would help him with the animals. Maybe that's why she was so affectionate with animals and never afraid of strange dogs. While I would tense up in the presence of the big, angry-looking beasts, Epp would cry out *"kutsu, kutsu"*[*] and soon they would be kissing each other and holding hands. She even cared for a stray cat and her newborn kitten that lived in a gutter near our apartment. Epp would bring the alley cats scraps of smoked fish and stroke them behind the ears.

In all of Epp's stories, Papa was calm and kind. He was like Santa Claus, old, wise, jolly, and good to his animals.

My grandfathers did not remind one of Santa Claus. Frank, my mother's father, never got to be old and wise. He died before I was born. Jerry, my father's father, was old when he died, but was more grumpy than jolly. I would sit beside him at the dinner table, scared of accidentally kicking his bad leg – he broke it in the war and subsequent operations messed it up even more. If you accidentally touched his leg, he would holler.

Nobody ever taught me how to nurse sick chickens back to life, or how to help a cat give birth. Epp's Papa taught her. From the stories, he seemed like an ideal grandfather.

"Papa loves maps," Epp told me on the bus. "He used to collect them when I was little. I remember when I went to Tunisia, he told me, 'Epp, don't you know I have a map of Tunisia?' Why would a guy who grew up in the Soviet Union need a map of Tunisia? But if he went to a store and saw a map, he had to buy it."

"If Papa liked maps so much then how come he didn't study geography?" I asked.

"He wasn't allowed."

"I don't understand."

---

[*] 'Doggy, doggy' in Estonian.

"His father was in Siberia at that time, so he applied and they told him he couldn't study geography. I guess they figured that his family knew enough geography already. He attended veterinary classes instead."

I swallowed young Karl's hard fate with some *kali* I had bought in Viljandi. The blossoming fields of Viljandi County passed by, some plowed by farmers on tractors. Youngsters walked along its roads eating ice cream in the hot sun. I liked being out here in the countryside. There were no American tourists or Maardu kids in need of bus money, just locals like our bus driver listening to accordion music on the radio.

"Did his father come back alive?"

"Aleksander came back from Siberia. I remember him. He died when I was about six."

"What was he like?"

"I remember him sleeping in his bed in the middle of the day with a bunch of cats and dogs to keep him warm. He was really bohemian."

Maybe that's why Epp liked animals so much. Not only did her grandfather Karl tend to them, her great-grandfather Aleksander even slept with them.

❋ ❋ ❋

We missed a connecting bus that would take us to Sürgavere village where Karl and Laine, Epp's grandmother, lived. Instead, we took another bus that took us somewhere close. It dropped us off at the intersection of two country roads where we could, according to Epp, walk on the hot gravel the 5 kilometers to Sürgavere.

"I have walked to their place from here," Epp said. "It won't take too long."

Epp, our unborn baby, and I were alone out here. The only sound was of birds chirping in the fields. One field was yellow with flowers, another green with wild rye. We held hands and walked down the middle of the road.

We were almost to Sürgavere when a bus pulled up alongside us. The driver opened its doors, and the accordion sounds from a local radio station beckoned us in.

"But we don't have tickets," Epp told the bus driver. She checked her wallet. "We are out of cash, too, sorry."

The bus driver was long and lean. He wore an old cap, glasses, and a vest, and looked as if he knew thing or two about animal husbandry. He nodded when Epp told him we had no money for tickets, but said nothing and waved us onboard the half-empty bus anyway. We got on.

Sitting alone in the fifth row was a man who looked familiar. I knew him from somewhere, but couldn't place it. He looked at us once, looked back out the window, then looked back again with a big grin. He laughed as Epp slid into the seat next to him. It was Papa.

Karl was a little round man with gray hair and those familiar high cheekbones. He wore a short-sleeved button-down shirt, pants, and shoes, clothes he had perhaps owned since Stalin decided his future would lay with sick animals rather than maps.

"This is Justin."

"Nice to meet you," I said in Estonian, holding out my hand.

"*Jah, jah,*"* Karl recognized me and shook it quickly and Epp opened her bag. I remembered that Epp had sent her grandparents photos of us from our fall trek through Europe.

"We brought you some candy," she said, depositing the bag of diabetic-friendly sweets in his hands.

"Of course, of course you brought me candy," he said, tearing open the bag and popping the first one in his mouth. "Oh, that's really good. Thank you, thank you."

Within a few minutes we rolled into Sürgavere past an old manor house flanked by well-tended green lawns and manicured hedges and trees.

"That's the *mõis*","** Epp said. "You know what a *mõis* is?"

Most places in Estonia were built around an old German manor house, I had read, and Sürgavere was no exception. In the not-so-distant past, the Baltic German nobility had owned most of the surrounding lands and employed most of the local Estonian people. Epp's predecessors would make their Baltic German overlords breakfast and dinner, wash their clothes, feed their horses, and plow their fields. The Baltic Germans would, in turn, ride around in carriages and go to dinner parties at other estates where they would socialize with fellow aristocrats to whom they were related, a few by marriage, a few by blood, and most by both.

These days, the Sürgavere *mõis* housed a school. It was another case of the Estonians taking over the deserted buildings of their former overseers and making them their own.

---

*   'Yes, yes' in Estonian.
**   'Manor house' in Estonian.

The bus left us at a bus stop near a cement-building with a sign that read simply *Kauplus*[*]. In Estonia, lots of stores had signs like that. Their signs didn't say 'Karl's Store' or 'Sürgavere Store'– they just said 'Store'. In Tallinn, our apartment was surrounded by flower shops, all of which had the same name – 'Flowers'. There was also a store nearby that sold buttons called 'Buttons' and a donut shop called the 'Donut Shop'.

Why did they have such simple names? Did Estonians lack creativity? In New York, a florist might have a memorable name like 'Simply Elegant'. Here, if they sold flowers, that's what they wrote on the sign.

We walked up the long gravel driveway to Karl and Laine's house. It was next to a large ugly Soviet-era building, a mini-*mõis* that probably served as a local recreational center.

"It used to be the center of a local collective farm," Epp said. "That's where my parents were married." I remembered the black and white photos of Andres and Aime from that day, almost 30 years before. Epp had been there, too. She was born six months later.

Karl and Laine lived on the first floor of a two-storey old house. Another family lived upstairs.

The front door to the house was open and the interior was cavernous and black. Out of the black hole that led to Karl and Laine's apartment, another old man stepped into the light.

"Epp?" he slurred, "Is that you?" The old-looking man squinted in the sun as if he hadn't been outside for days. He had

---

[*]   'Store' in Estonian.

long, graying hair and a beard. He wore a t-shirt, loose-fitting pants, and no shoes.

"Yes, Toivo, of course it's me," Epp said, wrapping her arms around him. He gave her a peck on the cheek.

"It's so good to see you," Toivo said. "I heard that you are going to have a little baby."

"Our baby is due in January, so we still have a long way to go."

"Come inside," Toivo said. "Mom made lunch."

"You can see the Tulevs have a bit of a Slavic touch," Epp whispered to me in the corridor. "They hug and kiss."

"Is Toivo your mom's older brother?" I asked, gesturing towards her graying uncle.

"No, Toivo is younger. He's in his mid-forties," she sighed. "It's just that he likes to drink and usually has no job. He's a really sweet person. He just likes to drink."

"Why?"

"Every Estonian family has its drunk. Toivo's ours."

❀ ❀ ❀

Epp's grandmother Laine couldn't remember my name. She flipped through a number of old letters until she found one where Epp had written it down.

"Ju-stin Pet-ro-ne," she read it aloud. "Ju-stin," Laine looked at me. "Maybe we can call you 'Sass' instead?"

"Sass?"

"It's a nickname for Aleksander," Epp said.

"That's fine with me," I shrugged. "I can be Sass."

To me, Laine looked like Epp, mostly because they shared the same distinguishing nose. Epp's mother had it, too. Maybe that nose had been handed down from generation to generation, so that if you went back in time to the *mōis* in the 16th century, you could easily spot Epp's ancestors.

Laine wore a sweater, pants, and had short gray hair. Like Karl, she was round and little. Neither of Epp's grandparents came up to my shoulders. Their apartment was definitely a dry, dark, warm, Hobbit-like hole, where old pensioners could horde maps and sugar-free candy.

Epp had shown me photos of her early childhood, much of it spent here with Karl and Laine while her mother Aime finished college in Tallinn. From these photos, I recognized everything in the apartment – the dark wooden bookshelves, the ancient green wall paper, the dusty curtains, and the modest tables and couches. It was as if it was frozen in 1975. In a few years, I thought, they could open up a museum here to show people what life was like in the mid-20th century.

Epp sat down and began to talk to Papa while Toivo disappeared into a back hallway. Mamma Laine was busy carrying food from the depths of the kitchen to the dimly lit living area.

I got lost among Karl's walls of books. The first bunch that caught my eye was a series called *Välispanoraam*[*]. It was an annual publication. Each one had the same cover, a group of gray old men sitting in a conference room before a bust of Lenin. From 1973 to 1983, the world around them changed, but the

---

[*]   'Foreign panorama' in Estonian.

aged decision makers on the cover of a book about international affairs stayed the same.

Then there were the volumes and volumes of books by one author or the other. Karl had the complete works of Balzac, Gorky, and Tammsaare, thick collections that ran over 12 volumes each.

"Have you read all those volumes of Tammsaare?" I asked Karl while Epp showed him photos of our life in Tallinn.

"More or less," he said.

"How about Balzac?"

"Not really," he chuckled.

Next I turned my attention to another bookcase. Here there were piles of maps and a stack of dictionaries: Estonian-Russian, Estonian-German, Estonian-Swedish, Latvian-Estonian, Russian-Polish, German-Czech.

"How many languages do you speak?" I asked Karl.

"I know Estonian, Russian, and German the best," he answered. "Not much English though."

"How did you learn them?"

"My father spoke to us in Russian and my mother spoke to us in Estonian," he said. "Naturally, I speak both. I learned German in school." Karl had a slow, deliberate way of speaking. I noticed that I understood almost everything he said, although it was all in Estonian.

"If your father was Russian, how did he wind up here?"

Karl paused, as if he was gauging how much family history he wanted to share with me.

"He was born in a place called Vyatka in the Ural Mountains. On the map, though, it's not called that anymore. Now they call it Kirov for one Soviet politician. When he was about 20, he wanted some adventure, so he joined the army."

I tried to imagine Karl's father Aleksander all those years ago at the end of tsarist times, so bored that he would enlist in the army in the middle of World War I.

"They were mobilized and sent to the front, but then the revolution happened. At first, he was in the Red Army, but then he was captured and put the next day into the White Army under General Nikolai Yudenich. They were based in Estonia and could not leave. When the war was over, naturally he couldn't go back to Russia. The Estonians took away their weapons and sent them to work in the countryside. That's how he met my future mother Adeele. He learned Estonian and he became partly Estonian – he even joined a conservative party called *Isamaaliit*. When the new war started, he joined *Omakaitse*, the home guard."

It turned out I wasn't the first foreigner to marry into Epp's family. It was odd that they decided to call me Sass – his nickname – as well.

"He knew they wanted to get him," Karl continued. "He changed his jobs and moved around in Estonia after the war. He even decided to move back to Russia for some time and hide there. But it was too late. They caught him on January 30th 1946. I'll never forget the date. He didn't come back for more than 10 years."

Karl told his father's story, but he didn't get upset, maybe because it had a happy ending. Aleksander came back. A lot of his friends' fathers probably didn't.

"What was it like living in a bilingual family?" I asked.

"When I was a child we lived in a mixed area," Karl answered. I was born in Värska, in southeast corner of Estonia called Setomaa, and I went to school in Petseri. With my father we spoke Russian, with mother and in school we spoke Estonian, and with the other kids and in the village we spoke Seto, a language related to Estonian. Father ran a store and spoke all these languages. We even had Russian names and were baptized in the Orthodox Church. I was 'Karp' and Leo was 'Leonid.'"

"Who's Leo?"

"Leo is his younger brother," said Epp. "Papa had three brothers. Leo is still alive, but Endel died a few years ago. What Russian name did Endel have?"

"Endel was Elias. It's another old Orthodox name used in baptisms," Karl answered.

"And their last name was 'Dujev,'" Epp said. "When they had the names campaigns in the '30s, they changed it to 'Tulev.'"

"Yes," Papa added, "We changed it exactly in the summer before I went to the first grade. My parents thought it would be easier for me if I had an Estonian name."

I had read that in the 1930s, the Estonian state encouraged its citizens to adopt Estonian-language names. At the time, many Estonian families still bore the German names that the manor owners had given them. Others, like Aleksander Dujev, took advantage of the campaign to better fit in. From Dujevs came Tulevs, from Schwarzbergs came Saluveers, and of Landmans – Laine's maiden name – were made Laanemaas.

What would my Estonian name be? I wondered. Peterson? But Petrone was so much better. It was a spicy gift from my Italian forebears.

Laine entered the room with two steaming metal pots, one held sausages, the other potatoes. Luckily there would be no meat jelly.

We all set around the table and I spotted a strip of strong Estonian mustard on my plate. One tiny bit of mustard could flavor three potatoes.

As we ate, Laine passed around old photos. I saw for the first time Aleksander and his Estonian wife Adeele-Helena. With dark hair and narrow eyes, Adeele looked more like an old Navajo Indian woman than the stereotype of the blond, blue-eyed Estonian. In some photos she wore a scarf on her head. I imagined her to be a country woman who knew how to harvest potatoes and patch up old clothes. Alexander, with his far-back hairline and high cheekbones, looked like a real character. In fact, he reminded me of a famous historical figure.

"He looks just like Lenin!"

As soon as the words passed my lips, I realized that I made a mistake. I could have said Aleksander looked like any other Russian – Tchaikovsky, Chekhov, Dostoyevsky.

Karl chewed his potatoes and shrugged. I didn't think I offended him.

"Adeele said each of her three sons married a different kind of woman," Laine said. "Endel's wife was the smartest, Leo's wife was the prettiest, and Karl's wife was the wealthiest." I took it to mean that Adeele didn't think much of Laine's intellect or looks.

Laine grinned for a second and seemed to enjoy her dig at her mother-in-law. She passed around more photos. There were childhood pictures of Epp's mother and her two uncles. In one photo little baby Toivo had his mouth open.

"It's an old omen," Laine said. "When a child's mouth is open in a photo, he grows up to be a drunk."

Toivo sat beside her and seemed content to eat lunch. He almost looked normal, except I noticed his hands were shaking.

"So you know we are going to get married," Epp told her grandparents.

"Yes," Papa said and smiled.

"We were going to anyway. Justin, um, Sass is already beyond the legal limit of the time he can spend in Estonia. We are going to file for a living permit after we get married and hope he gets it."

"Are you nervous?" Toivo asked me. It was the first thing he said during lunch.

"A little," I told him.

"I am sure they'll let him stay," Epp reassured her family. "Could you imagine if they didn't? It would be so cruel."

"But people *are* cruel," Toivo slurred. "You are just a name on a piece of paper to them."

He may have been right, but what could I do about it? I would just have to suppress my anxiety with some *astelpaju* juice, a smooth-tasting, fruit drink made from orange seabuckthorn berries which I had never before encountered.

"Where's the toilet?" I asked.

"It's out in the hallway near the front door," Epp said. "They share it with the neighbors."

I left to find the toilet. It wasn't hard to locate. The dark, humid room stunk of piss. At first I thought about holding it, but decided that if it was ok for Karl, it was ok for me. I'd live. I took one last gasp of fresh air and entered.

The walls were paneled with old wood. Scraps of old newspaper hung on a rusty nail, for toilet paper I guessed. A rust-covered metal toilet bowl sat before me. I had no idea how old it was. I was sure Aleksander himself had used it a few times. He was almost a quarter of a century dead. Maybe he was the last foreigner before me to use it.

The bowl stunk. I breathed through my mouth instead of my nose. Hungry flies buzzed in my ears. There was no handle to flush, because there was no plumbing. This was just an outhouse turned into an in house. I got out of there as fast as I could, and returned to the living room for more food and family history.

❋ ❋ ❋

"I have to tell you that I really love you," Epp said as on the bus. It was late in the day. We would bring candles to the graveyard where Epp's mother was buried.

"Why?" Epp didn't tell me she loved me every day.

"You haven't said one word to me about their toilet or how poor they are."

"The toilet was kind of old."

"Could you imagine if any of your relatives would use it?"

I tried to imagine what my mother would do in my situation. I guessed she would ask my father to drive her to a gas station where a cleaner toilet was on offer. She would probably tell all her friends and colleagues about the toilet for a week, too.

"I think a lot of them would refuse," I said.

"But you are different. Why are you different?"

"I don't know. Papa uses it every day. I guess it's not life threatening."

"They are old people. They shouldn't have to live that way."

"Don't they get pensions?"

"They do. Pretty small ones."

"Can't anybody help?"

"Mom died, Toivo's a drunk, and their other son Vello is away in Finland. Papa has diabetes and Mama isn't going to install a new toilet."

"Maybe we could help?"

"I have offered to help them many times. They always refuse. They are too proud. And they are used to life as it is."

I was silent. I thought of the well-heeled young Tallinners in their black cars and office jobs and indoor plumbing. A large gap existed between their life and Epp's grandparents' lifestyle.

"It's like they say, there are two Estonias," Epp steamed. "There are the winners and the losers. I was only 18 years old when I became the editor of a monthly magazine. I had a pretty big salary and I was only a year out of high school! I bought my first home in my early 20s. I traveled and spent my money on air tickets and hotels. I am sure my Papa would have liked to travel, too."

"But why is it like that? Why are old people poor?"

"Our generation is just lucky, I guess," Epp said. "We were young and flexible, we learned fast. We wanted our business partners to be young, too. Who wanted to mess with the pensioners? They worked their entire lives for the Soviet state and now all they get is a little pension money each month."

We spent the rest of our short bus trip in silence. Sitting there, I realized that most foreigners who came to Estonia probably never made it out of the picturesque Old Town of Tallinn They never saw its old rusty toilets or ate lunch with its drunken uncles. I wondered if I would tell anybody else about this other Estonia, or if I would keep it to myself.

Suure-Jaani town was built around an appealing country lake overlooked by a sober Lutheran Church. According to a sign, some kind of Christian church had been here since at least 1300, less than a century after the German conquest. It had been badly damaged in both the Livonian and Great Northern Wars. The current church dated from 1767. Epp's mother, her father's parents, and other relatives were all buried in the church's sleepy shadow.

We stepped into a shop near the bus stop to buy flowers and candles to bring to the cemetery.

"Do you ever bring candles to your grandfather's grave?" Epp asked.

"I haven't visited it since he was buried."

"Never? Not once?"

"I don't know where he is. After they buried him, my grandmother found out that there wasn't enough room in the plot for them to rest side by side. So she bought a new, bigger plot and had him moved. Now she's so old she can't remember where he is either."

"It's creepy. I don't get it. People here visit cemeteries all the time to bring flowers and candles. You should see it in Christmas. It's all lit up. It's really beautiful."

Just then a young couple walked by. One of them looked familiar.

"Epp?" the big man said.

"Tere!" It was Janek, one of the guys from the "Proffessional Building" Service in London. Epp knew his girlfriend. Her people were from Suure-Jaani, too.

"We're visiting the old folks," he said. "How do you like living in Estonia?" he asked me. "Can you manage?"

"I am doing ok. It's a lot better in summer," I said.

Janek smiled at me, but something seemed different. He had a mouth full of healthy-looking white teeth. He was like an advertisement for toothpaste.

We let them buy flowers and said goodbye. Estonia was so small, I was sure I would see them again. Soon we were on our way up the hill, past the lake, to the forested cemetery.

"Janek used to have really bad teeth. Now his teeth are perfect. What happened?" I asked Epp.

"Working in the UK pays off," she said.

"But why did he have such bad teeth. How come your dad has bad teeth?"

"The state health insurance covers everything but dental costs."

The cemetery was spread out on the crest of a hill and surrounded by old mossy stone walls. The gravestones differed according to age. Some were simple wrought iron crosses, others were stone obelisks with the names of whole families. As I moved deeper into the cemetery, I read off the names of former sweethearts: Juhan and Mari, Peeter and Liidia.

Between the rows of stones and crosses were ancient trees that created a heaven of greenery above. And from its center, you could see the peaceful lake below. I imagined that all the souls of Suure-Jaani swam in that lake, their stories and memories mingling with the cool water.

I had never seen a cemetery like it before. Many of the graveyards where I grew up were fields of economically placed stones, usually located far from the main streets. There were no trees, no stone walls, and no scenic views.

"I used to go swimming in there next to the graves all the time," Epp said. "People thought I was weird, but it's so peaceful and kind of mysterious here, especially at sunset."

I followed Epp down along a path of graves to a small, flat stone. On it was carved her mother's name: *Aime Saluveer 1954–1995*. She crouched over the stone and went to work picking up the plastic from old candle containers and pulling out weeds and dead flowers. It was interesting to see how much work went into taking care of a little piece of land. The work seemed therapeutic.

"Papa said he came here recently," she said discarding the wilted flowers. "They come once a week."

After she was finished tidying the plot, I helped her light the candle, which she nestled next to the stone, and dug out the earth with my hands so that she could plant the flowers in front.

I looked down at Aime's stone. Maybe she knew somewhere that she was going to be a grandmother again.

By the way, what's the date today?" Epp asked.

"May 26th 2003."

"Her birthday is next week. If she was still alive, she would be turning 49," she stared at the stone. "She would still be young."

I looked up into the trees and breathed in the cool air coming off the pond. It seemed like a good place to spend eternity.

THE REPUBLIC
OF SOUTH ESTONIA

---

*Epp was an Estonian. I was an American with an
Italian last name. We were expecting an adorable tita**,
but didn't know what to call it.*

When we broached the topic with Epp's father Andres in Karksi, the man of few words pounded his fists on the table and
made his opinion known.

"Karl Erik!" he declared, as if announcing the entry of a
Swedish king. Karl was Epp's mother's father. Erik was Andres'
father's name.

"Karl Erik *Petrone*? That sounds a little too Viking to me," I
whispered to Epp.

"Maybe it's a little too Scandinavian for us," Epp told her
father. Andres' expression said *How come nobody ever listens
to me?* He opened his mouth to say something, but took a swig
from a can of beer instead.

"What was your grandfather's name?" Epp asked.

---

*   'Baby' in Estonian.

"His birth name was Gennaro, but everyone called him Jerry."

"Jerry? Like *Tom and Jerry*? That won't work. We have got to give it a name that people can say both in Estonia and in America," Epp said. "I don't want to be in a situation where my grandmother has to have her great-grandchild's name written down on a sheet of paper so she can remember it."

"Here," Andres said, handing us a calendar. "Pick one."

We sat outside the Karksi house in the sun. In the light I could see the place desperately needed work. There was no siding on the house – in many places, paper insulation still stuck out from the walls. Andres rebuilt most of it after it burned down, Epp had told me. He just hadn't finished the job yet.

We looked at the calendar. A number of names were written under each date.

"In Estonia, people not only have birthdays, they have name days," Epp said.

"What do people do on name days?"

"Nothing. I think it's just some tradition they stole from Finland. Let's start from January."

We flipped to the first page of the calendar. The names for January 1st were Algo, Alo, Esmo, Uno, and Uuno. The names for January 2nd were Algi, Esme, and Esmi. I scanned through the month for anything that might work in the United States. Kanut? Too medieval. Feliks? Too 19th century. Osvald? The guy who shot President Kennedy. Õnneleid?

"Who names their kid Õnneleid?"

"I don't know. Let's just leave that one off our list and keep looking."

I scanned through the following months with little success.

"Most of these names are useless. Meinhard? Aksel? Voldemar? Will the baby carry a sword and slay dragons?"

"But Paul could work. So could Martin. My great-grandfather was Martin," Epp said.

We pressed on and soon we had compiled a short list of names that were socially acceptable in both countries. For girls we chose Roosi, Mari, and Liis. For boys, we selected Paul, Martin, and Peeter. Roosi was cute, but I wasn't sold on it. Paul wasn't my favorite either, but it hadn't kept Paul McCartney from selling millions of records. And grandma Laine wouldn't have to write it down on a sheet of paper to remember it. It would suffice.

"How about Paul?" Epp asked her father.

"Paul?" Andres shrugged his shoulders, as if to say, *Name him whatever you like, he's your kid.* Andres wore a stained t-shirt that was too short for his belly. He had on a pair of work pants and held a chainsaw.

"You keep looking," he said and actually smiled. "I'm going to go cut some wood."

He headed off towards the barns, looking content at last. For guys in the south Estonian countryside, I guessed, drinking beer and cutting wood were among life's greatest pleasures.

In the 2003 film *"Made in Estonia"* a representative of NATO arrives in a rural Estonian town. A high school band welcomes him and he is ushered into a school auditorium. One of the locals, a pencil-thin radio host with a Hitler moustache wearing a sports coat, ugly t-shirt, neon green trousers, and sandals, greets the NATO emissary:

"Sir, we are delighted to have you here. Welcome to the Republic of South Estonia."

The Republic of *South* Estonia? I got the joke. South Estonia is poor, backward, and undeserving of being in any alliance. Still, I thought that south Estonians must be really pigheaded to think they are so different from their northern neighbors. Surely, there were plenty of poor, backward, badly dressed radio hosts in Tallinn too.

Over time, I started to understand that South Estonia was a country to itself. You could bus between Viljandi, Karksi-Nuia, Tartu, Pärnu, and Põlva, and never once think that any other part of Estonia even existed. Tallinn was a distant metropolis teeming with foreigners. Saaremaa was an island out there somewhere in the ocean. And Narva? It might as well be in Russia.

❀ ❀ ❀

After visiting Epp's father in Karksi, we took a bus to the university town Tartu. Since she was pregnant, Epp's master's paper was now of less concern. She needed to see a doctor to get a note that would allow her to delay her studies.

Meantime I had stopped e-mailing the school in Valparaíso. Maybe dragging a newborn baby to Chile was a little irresponsible after all. We would stay in Estonia instead, at least until *tita* came. Our dreams of world travel would have to wait.

We actually came to Estonia so Epp could get her master's but, as a famous Englishman once said, life is what happens to you when you're busy making other plans.

In Tartu, we stayed with Eva, and their family had a surprise for us that afternoon – five tiny little kittens. They were born only a day before to the family cat.

I watched as the little blind babies – some orange, some gray, some brown – fought with one another for access to their mother's tired nipples. There just wasn't enough space for all of them. They were sleeping between the stove and a cabinet, where it was dark and warm.

"Do you want one?" Eva asked us.

"I am not sure," Epp held a gray one in her hands. "Justin, what do you think?"

When I was growing up, my family owned several cats, some more neurotic than others. The first one got hit by a car. The next two were still alive at my parents' house, though they slept all day. When I thought about the kitten, all that came to mind was two words: litter box. I had a feeling that cleaning the cat box was "man's work" in Estonia.

"Our apartment is too small," I said.

"And we have a baby coming," Epp agreed. "We shouldn't take one."

Epp went out and I stayed at home with Eva, Simona, and Mamma. Pets, though, was not at home. He had finally received his call to go to sea, and had flown to Spain just days before to join a fishing vessel. He drew a picture of a boat for Simona to explain his new job to her. It now hung on the wall beside her bed. Such things were typical in Estonian families.

Pets' mother, known as Mamma, spent most of her days inside watching Spanish-language soap operas. She was a cheerful old woman and I had been in her small room a few times to look at the old photos on the wall. There was even a photo of Mamma as a young woman. But there was no photo of Pets' father.

"Did you know Pets' father?" I asked Eva.

"Johannes? No, he died before I met Pets."

"Was he sick?"

"He wasn't young, he was in his seventies."

I did some arithmetic in my head. Eva had been together with Pets since at least a year before Simona was born. I had seen photos of their courtship: there were late night parties, early morning parties, mid-afternoon parties. Life had been one big party until Eva stopped partying and started incubating.

But if Johannes had been in his seventies in the mid-90s, then he must have been born in the 1920s. That would make him an extremely ancient 50 year-old dad by Estonian standards. He was old enough to have been Pets' grandfather.

"But if his father was so old when he was born..."

"Johannes was drafted into the German Army," Eva said. "He spent 10 years in Siberia after the war. That's where he lost his hand."

Now I understood why he was a late father, and I understood some other things, too. Johannes had the best years of his life stolen from him. He had to start all over again in midlife. With his one hand and rough past, he must have made a strong impression for a little boy like Pets. Maybe that's why he seemed a little restless. Life was quick and sometimes painful. Better to enjoy it while it lasted.

❋ ❋ ❋

At night, Eva's place was as dark and warm as the cats' nest next to the oven. Between Mamma's cutlets, Eva's cakes, and the tropical temperatures, it was easy to slip into a deep sleep.

Early the next morning, I felt the hot sun hit my eyelids. It shone brightly through the window, and I pulled off the blanket and sat up on the couch. Epp snoozed beside me and, as far as I could tell, no one else was up. But how could that be? I was usually the one who slept in. I walked to the window and looked at the courtyard. The sun was so bright it had to be late morning, maybe even early afternoon.

I walked outside and out of the courtyard into the middle of Jaani Street and stood on the cobblestones. I eyed the city center and then turned towards Supilinn. No cars passed by. No pedestrians were around. All was silent and empty. It was if all of Tartu had been evacuated. I had woken up in a science fiction movie.

Worried, I returned to the apartment and searched through my bag for my mobile phone. I had to see what time it was. 10 am? That's what it looked like. I pushed aside my clothes and journal, and felt around for the elusive phone. At last I grasped its rectangular shape, pulled it out, and looked at the time. It was 4:43 am.

I knew the days would get longer, but I had no idea it could be bright as midday at a quarter to five in the May morning. Just months before the days were mostly night. Now the nights were mostly day. No wonder the people of this country seemed so numb to the world. They lived in the physical embodiment of a mood disorder.

I paused in the hallway to contemplate space and time. Then I heard a door creak open behind me. It was Mamma. Her head as always was wrapped in an old headscarf. She was carrying an empty bucket and stepped quickly away when she noticed me. She looked anxious. The bucket had drops of water running down its sides.

"Sorry if I scared you," I tried to find right words in Estonian. "It's so bright out."

Mamma said nothing. She nodded and bit her lip, placed the wet bucket in the kitchen to dry, and went back into her room. I returned to our bed and crawled back beside Epp to get a few more hours of rest.

As we ate breakfast five hours later, I told Epp about my adventures in the early morning light. Eva had gone out to do some shopping, Simona was watching cartoons, and Mamma was in her room, probably watching another soap opera.

I walked into the kitchen to get another bag of milk. Standing beside the refrigerator, I spied the mother cat's tail poking out from beside the stove. I kneeled down to glimpse those cute kittens again. It was such a shame we couldn't take one home, but I was sure they'd all find people to care for them.

As I crouched down, I saw there was only one little gray kitten nursing on the mother cat's vacant nipples. Not only that, the mother cat looked confused. *Where are my babies*, the cat seemed to say. *What have you done with them?*

I put the bag of milk in the plastic container, cut a corner off, walked back to the living room, and lightened my cup of morning coffee.

"What happened to all the baby cats?" I asked. "There's only one in there. Did they give the rest away already?"

"Oh, I think they went to sea school," Epp said.

"*Sea school*?" I imagined the little kittens dressed in navy uniforms, learning how to sail.

"Mamma got rid of them," she said under her breath.

"Got rid of them?"

Suddenly, I put it all together. Mamma in the morning. The missing kittens. The wet bucket. They had been euthanized. Simona's kind grandmother had probably bundled them up in a bag, loaded in a heavy rock, and done the awful deed in the hallway water closet. The sea cadets were executed at sunrise. I wondered how she chose the lucky survivor.

"So where *are* they?"

"Probably in the garbage," Epp snapped.

"She threw them in the garbage?"

"Or maybe she buried them. Why are you asking me about this? I don't know. And I don't like either what happened. When I was a child, I cried after finding out what grownups had done to the kittens."

"Why don't they just get the cat neutered so that no more kitties have to go to sea school?" All our pet cats in New York had been fixed. It seemed like the responsible thing for pet owners to do.

"They don't bother, I guess. And some people say it's unnatural," Epp said. "I don't want to talk about it anymore, okay? That's just how things are done here."

Another day, another south Estonian experience.

Amanda placed a wooden barrel on a round table near the backdoor to her house. It was filled to the middle with warm dough that stank of rising yeast. I positioned my body so that the sun shone directly on the dough and there was no shadow in the frame, then snapped a few quick photos.

Epp was on assignment in Põlvamaa and I was the photographer. This was a *turismitalu*, a tourism farm, a quiet nook in the south Estonian countryside where city people like us could escape for the weekend and relax with a little bread making during the day and sauna at night.

Epp's magazine was regularly offered free trips to travel destinations like these. We took the bus south from Tartu earlier that day and were picked up by Arvo at the Põlva city bus station. Arvo and his wife Eela ran another *turismitalu* near Amanda's. We left our bags there after Eela, a friendly country lady with short brown hair, gave us a quick tour. Then they drove us over to Amanda's place. She was charged with giving us a south Estonian culinary lesson.

All of them were old. With his wispy hair and sharp features, Arvo looked like a gray fox. Amanda had big rosy cheeks, lots of energy, and reminded me of a plump hen. Her husband Reinhard meantime was the slow rooster, quietly watching all unfold in the distance. That's how most Estonian couples were. The women were bustling powerhouses. The men were barely there.

Amanda's introductory course to the southern Estonian kitchen had been lunch. She fed us refreshing cucumber salad and pork roasted so long it nearly dissolved in our mouths. It was followed with loaves of sweet bread and butter. We washed

the meal down with a refreshing mix of water and diced rhubarb. By the time Amanda was ready to teach Epp how to make
bread the old-fashioned way, I could barely stand.

Epp and Amanda both wore aprons and tied white scarfs
around their heads. Soon they were in the thick of the dough,
kneading it until it was ready to be shaped into loaves or rolls
and fed into the oven. The smell of the yeast was in the air. Epp
was covered from fingertip to elbow in sticky dough.

"You have to put your elbow into it," Amanda lectured Epp.
"Making bread is hard work. You have to keep doing it if you
want it to come out good."

"*Aitüma*," Epp said to Amanda after the lesson. She told
me that it was how south Estonians gave thanks.

Later Amanda and Reinhard showed us around the farm.
Amanda took the lead, while Reinhard sat on a step and tin-
kered with an old mandolin. He saw my interest and handed it
to me. I had never played one before, but managed to pluck out
an elementary tune before handing it back.

"Not bad for a beginner," he said. "Do you play guitar?"

"I'm still learning," I said. I bought a red acoustic in Tartu.
On random nights I would sit up in the bathroom teaching myself new chords.

The day was hot, and the smell of the pungent manure on
the fields was a constant reminder that we were deep in the
country. To these people, the aroma of hot shit was as comforting as freshly-baked bread.

"I love it out here," Epp said. She still had on her little white
wimple and apron. "I am so tired of the city. I could just take a
sauna right now and go swimming in that pond."

She pointed at a man-made pond with murky water. It was the size of a swimming pool, the kind people had in their back-yards in my parents' neighborhood in New York. While the water in those pools was always crystal clear, the banks of the pond were muddy, and the air was thick with mosquitoes and dragonflies. The surface of the pond was black with tadpoles.

"You want to go *swimming* in there? I think the lake back at Arvo and Eela's was a little cleaner."

"I like swimming with the tadpoles. They tickle you. It's so romantic."

Next Amanda showed us the sauna.

"This is the oldest house on the property," she announced. I looked inside the tiny wooden building. There was one room for the sauna, and one room for everything else. The walls of the sauna were black with soot. The other room was musty and warm. Everything smelled like smoke. I imagined that if I stayed long enough in here, so would I.

"They always built the sauna first, because it was the most important," Amanda said. She hurried along to set up her old wooden loom. Epp had learned how to make bread. Now it was time to make cloth. Our day in the life of a South Estonian would be very thorough; Amanda taught classes like these every day.

Epp and I meantime remained in the dark sauna.

"In the old days, a husband and wife would sauna once a week to get clean," she said. "They would make love, every Saturday after the sauna. They did everything in the sauna. Even their babies were born in here."

I leaned in to kiss her. Her old-fashioned headscarf rubbed against my face.

Forty years from now, we could be Reinhard and Amanda. We could settle our own farm somewhere in south Estonia and come to love the smell of hot manure and freshly-baked bread. Epp would grow rosier and plumper with every helping of rhubarb cake. I would acquire the same steady gate to my step that Reinhard the rooster had, and sit beside the barn plucking out tunes on an old mandolin.

Each day, we would get up, knead the dough, spin the cloth, take a sauna, swim in the pond, and send the kittens to sea school (well, maybe not that). Before bed, we would say *aitüma* to God for allowing us to live in such a special place.

WEDDING
DAY

"A man once asked me to marry him," Pille said.
"I asked him, 'Why? Why do you want to get married?'
He had no response."

"So did you marry him?" I asked.

"Ha," she mocked my question. "No."

Pille ran her fingers through her brown hair, and looked down at Epp and me on the edge of *Hirvepark* in Tallinn. We were having a picnic to celebrate the big changes in our life. She was an old friend of Epp's – a 34 year-old lawyer who worked for an insurance firm. Pille was tough and opinionated. She was also opposed to the idea of marriage.

Decades before, Pille's attitude would have seemed rebellious. In 2003, it was conventional. Most of the young adults around me never had a good word to say about marriage. People our age bungee jumped off bridges and went skydiving. Pille herself had taken off for Central Asia as a wild teenager and hiked the back streets of North African cities in recent years. But utter the word marriage and they were all terrified.

Estonia was still home to some of the youngest newlyweds in Europe. The average age for men was 28. For women it was 25. In Finland, the corresponding averages were 31 and 28. But Estonia's averages had been rising. Back in the Soviet days, an unmarried, childless 28-year-old woman like Epp would have been considered an old maid.

"Well, I wish you two the best of luck," Pille said that day in the park. She tried to be sincere, but I didn't believe her. It wasn't her fault. Whenever it came to marriage, the specter of certain doom choked the air. We needed luck because we were doing something foolish. We were making a promise that was hard to keep in an age of endless self indulgence.

For Epp and me, the moment of reckoning was just days away. We would get married by the city and then take a bus down to South Estonia for a family party aboard a boat on Viljandi Lake. Epp's office would hold a party as well where friends like Pille could attend. Estonians were pretty relaxed when it came to wedding traditions. In the old days, they would hold three-day parties on the farm, Epp said. Nowadays everything was improvised.

"What kind of hors d'oeuvres should we get – the ones with artichoke or the ones with avocado?" Epp had asked the day before. We were in a restaurant in Viljandi trying to prepare the menu for our party.

"I don't know."

"Please. Why do I have to make all these decisions?"

"Why don't we get both?"

"Good idea."

Most of the answers I gave her about our party were spontaneous like that.

"How long should the boat sail for: an hour, two hours, or three hours?" she asked.

"Two hours," I decided at random. When in doubt, choose the answer that felt right.

In a way, that's how I wound up in Estonia. That's how I wound up with a child on the way. That's how I wound up within days of marriage. Life is not just the decisions we make, I concluded. Most decisions, after all, had only temporary effects. Instead, a big chunk of life was up to some unknown ingredient; the hidden conveyer belt that brought me to northern Europe and left me here to fulfill my destiny.

Even after living together with Epp for months in an apartment that featured an old Orthodox icon and portrait of Sai Baba, religion was still foreign to me. But I now believed deeply in my fate. I accepted that on June 6, Epp and I would be married. I decided to ignore all the nagging impulses that made my peers quiver in fear each time they heard the dreaded 'm' word. And when I killed every last little bastard of self-doubt hiding in my soul, I felt at ease.

We bought our rings at a jewelry shop on Kentmanni Street on the morning of June 6. I was in a clear state of mind. I had no hang over to sleep off because there had been no bachelor party – because I had no friends in Estonia, rock stars notwithstanding.

And where were my few friends? Eamon was in Boston. CJ was in Los Angeles. Rory was in Seattle. Dave was in Florida. Only Marc was still in New York. They couldn't have made it to a party on such short notice.

"Wait, *when* are you getting married?" Ivan asked at the office the day before.

"Tomorrow."

"Then what are you doing here?"

"The same thing I do every day."

"But aren't you going to have a party? Before I got married," Ivan shook his head, "we'll, let's just say that things got a little out of hand."

"I am sure they did."

I was sure Ivan and his legions of friends emptied a store's full of liquor and showed the stumbling British stag party drunks in Tallinn's town hall square the meaning of the words 'shit faced.' But what was I going to do? Hit the strip clubs alone? I didn't even want to.

In the jewelry shop, the clerk asked us what our price range was.

"The least expensive," Epp giggled.

Her answer made me laugh too. The words might as well have been, "I do." My mother told me that I could buy Epp an expensive engagement ring *post facto*. "Don't worry," she had said. "You can get her something in a decent price range for your anniversary in the future. Maybe your father and I will help you out."

But Epp didn't want an expensive ring. "If they really want to waste some money on us, they can buy us plane tickets somewhere cool, like India," she dismissed the idea.

That was fine with me, because though I was now ok with marriage, fatherhood, and the creeping Estonianization of my life, I still hadn't gotten used to American wedding protocol.

Hosting a big party? Wearing uncomfortable clothes? Obeying confusing rules? Couldn't I just hire somebody else to do that part for me? At least we didn't have to have an American-sized wedding in Estonia; our boat party was supposed to be small and quick.

The jeweler pulled out a display of gold wedding rings. We tried on different ones until we found rings that fit. I looked down at my left ring finger, now crowned by the heavy metal. *Do I really have to wear one of these for the rest of my life?*

"Don't worry," Epp read my expression. "You'll get used to it. Trust me, I know."

"I know you know." I remembered Epp's divorce. For the first time all day, I felt a little anxious.

The jeweler smiled again. She must have enjoyed watching nervous young couples like us. I removed my ring and she put it in a small paper bag for us to carry to the city government office.

Tiina from Harju county government officiated over our wedding ceremony. This time she seemed unfazed by my Italian origins. Instead she was friendly, even sweet. She read us a poem, most of which I didn't understand. The only word I hung on was *armastus*, love.

Towards the end of the ceremony, Tiina asked me a question, to which I replied, "yes." She asked Epp the same question and she also said, "yes." Then we kissed and someone from city government took our picture and gave us a bouquet of flowers. We signed our names in a book. My name stayed the same. Epp Väljaots became Epp Petrone.

"That's it? You just sign your name in a book and you're married?"

I didn't understand. This was the action that inspired fear in the hearts of millions of people all over the world? Go to a building, listen to some poetry, kiss your loved one, and sign your name in a book? That's it? That's what all the goddamn fuss is about?

Epp didn't respond. As usually she was a few steps ahead of me. We were headed back to the apartment to pick up our bags. If we didn't hurry, we might miss our bus to Viljandi. We passed the security perimeter around the American embassy and turned up the steps to our building.

"Where do you think you're going?" a man called out to me from the street. I spun around. It was my colleague Ivan, and around his neck hung the newspaper's high-quality camera.

"Stay right there," he said. I held up the bouquet of flowers and grinned through three flashes from the camera.

"I've got to go cover a protest on *Toompea* now," Ivan said. "But congratulations to you both."

"You always describe him as being so cynical," said Epp. "He seems really romantic."

✽ ✽ ✽

We got to the bus on time, but I was soaked with sweat. I carried all the bags these days because Epp was worried about losing the baby. Supposedly, any heavy lifting could undo biology's will. I didn't understand the secret forces at work, but I knew that I had to help her.

"I'm thirsty," Epp said on the bus. We were about an hour out of town, sitting in the front seat, still wearing our wedding clothes. "I feel like I am going to pass out."

"Oh Christ."

"Please get me water, Justin. I'm thirsty, I'm afraid..."

I stood up on the bus and announced our predicament to the other passengers. "*Me vajama vesi! Minu naine on rasedus*[*]*!*"

In the subway trains of New York, crazy people made announcements all the time. Some even gave them money. But by standing up on that bus to Viljandi, I had broken unspoken Estonian rules: always keep your personal problems to yourself. Never ask others for help, even if your wife is pregnant and thirsty on a hot bus. If she's thirsty, it's your own fault for not buying water at the station.

I was met by looks of indifference. Nobody knew what to make of me. Who was this oddball and what did he want?

"Justin, please," Epp croaked and tugged on my shirt sleeve. "I need water or I'm going to..."

"Please, please!" I pleaded with the shocked passengers. "*Tema on väga rasedus. Me vajama vesi*[**]*!*"

---

[*]   'We to need water! My wife is pregnancy!' in broken Estonian.
[**]   'She is very pregnancy! We to need water,' in broken Estonian.

325

At last a blond teenager dug through her knapsack and handed us an unopened bottle of water. She handed it to me in silence, and I gave it to Epp who finished it in one gulp.

❀　❀　❀

We ate our first meal as husband and wife at a pub next to St. John's Church in Viljandi.

By now, it felt as if I was from this town. Even though I barely knew my way around the place, it was the town where Epp was born and the hub of Viljandimaa. We all belonged here: the bartender working the taps, her hair pulled back in a ponytail; the mechanic drinking his blues away, his work overalls stained with grease; the aspiring actor in the corner studying his lines; and the newlyweds in the booth by the window, getting accustomed to the rings on their fingers.

"I'm worried about going to America," Epp said. "It's not good for me to have too much stress. I have had one miscarriage before. I might..."

"Well, what are you stressed out about?"

"I'm afraid of the party your mom is planning. It's starting to sound pretty big."

My mother had been busy in recent weeks trying to set up a family party to celebrate our marriage. It would be blessed in a church in a wedding-like ceremony, followed by a reception at a restaurant. I figured the wedding blessing was her way of dealing with the abrupt change in her younger son's life. She could sit around and ponder what she had done wrong to make me a husband and expectant father at 23, or she could console herself with event planning.

"She said that she would only invite a handful of people; just family and a few friends."

Epp toyed with her food. She didn't seem convinced.

"I'll talk to my mom tonight," I said. "I'm sure everything will be fine."

"You invited how many people?" I asked.

"100," my mother answered.

"That's a lot of people. I thought you said it was going to be a small party."

"It is small."

"A party with 100 people is small?"

"Think of all the people who have invited me to their kids' weddings," she said. "Of course I have to invite them to yours."

"But they didn't invite me." It was the truth. The first marriage I had attended in my life had been my own just hours before.

"Look, I didn't call you to talk about this stuff. I called to say congratulations on your wedding and..."

"Thanks, Mom."

"Epp is very nice. Based on my experience with your other girlfriends, you could have done a lot worse. I mean—"

"Justin, are you still talking?" Epp called out to me from our room. I was sitting in a chair in the hallway.

"Yeah, I am," I answered.

"Do you have to go?" my mother asked.

"We've been on the phone for about half an hour, Mom. Just finish what you were saying and we'll talk later."

"I just wanted to say that your father and I got married the same way. We had to get married for some real estate thing. We were married by a judge in a courtroom. We've made it for almost 25 years. And..."

"You got married because of some real estate thing?"

"Justin, you have been on the phone with her for 45 minutes," Epp now stood impatiently before me and whispered: "We have a party to organize for tomorrow and this is our wedding night, please."

I felt as if I were a doll being fought over by two little girls. Epp was pulling on my head. Mom was pulling on my legs. Epp wanted to connect with her husband on her wedding day. Mom wanted to connect with her son on his wedding day. It was impossible to sate their needs. No matter what I did, both would probably be annoyed.

"Ok, it's getting kind of late," I told my mother. "I have got to go."

"But I..."

"We can talk when we get back to Tallinn. We are in Viljandi and we need to arrange some things."

"Go, go," Mom sounded a little sad. "Tell her I said congratulations again." She hung up.

I felt guilty, but I understood Epp. It was our wedding day. Estonian men usually didn't talk with their mothers for 45 minutes on the phone. They usually didn't talk for 45 minutes in a row at all. If Epp hadn't stepped in, the length of the phone conversation could have easily stretched past an hour.

I was dealing with two strong women. Mom imagined herself to be the matriarchal don of an Italian family. She demanded respect, to organize parties as big as she liked, and to be listened to for as long as she could talk. Epp also liked to plan things, but she had no time for lavish parties or small talk. She was an industrious South Estonian girl who wanted to get things done. Her plans needed my attention. Perhaps there were some tough decisions to make, such as what music they should play on the boat.

❋ ❋ ❋

Papa Karl and Mamma Laine were the last ones aboard. They came with Aunt Salme to represent the Tulev-Laanemaa clan. Toivo the drunk didn't come. He stayed behind in Sürgavere. Vello? No one was sure of his whereabouts. The guest star of the boat party, though, was Epp's mysterious brother Priit. He said nothing as he walked up the ramp, save a brisk "Congratulations!" when he neared us.

"Thanks for coming," I held my hand out to Priit, my new brother-in-law. He gave it a strange look and then decided to shake it. "It's good to finally meet you," I said.

"Who? Me?" Priit looked around as if I was talking to someone else.

"Yes, you."

"Oh," he looked really confused. His expression said *who is this strange man and why does he want to shake my hand*? "Ok," he shrugged and stepped onboard.

I had never seen Priit before, but I had spoken to him on the phone a few times when he called Epp. I knew he had been in the army. I knew he had been unemployed. These days he worked in a match factory, packing matchboxes into shipment containers. He was thinking of switching jobs, though, Epp said. He had a friend at a pillow factory who said they might need an extra set of hands packing pillows into boxes.

Like too many Estonian guys, Priit was stuck working low-skilled jobs in an unforgiving country. If one wasn't careful, he could easily slip from having a few drinks each day after work to being a full-blown, dysfunctional alcoholic, just like too many Estonian guys.

I tried to focus on being a gracious host. Everybody said: "*Palju õnne.*" Andres stood there wearing sunglasses and gripped my hand. It occurred to me that I hadn't bothered to ask his daughter's hand in marriage. Did Estonians even do that? Well, I guess it was too late now. And what would happen if he said, 'No'?

"Eva says our father likes you," Epp whispered in my ear. She said, "He said that you seem like a normal person."

"I'm a normal person?" I had never been told that before.

"Nobody in our family is really normal," Epp said in a hushed voiced. "I guess it means that you are part of the family."

All of the Saluveers were there. Most of them shook my hand, but Uncle Tiit's wife Reeli, an English-teacher in Tallinn, gave me a strong hug and whispered in my ear: "Please, take care of our baby." I realized they had all known Epp since she was just a strong-willed child. The urgent way Reeli gripped me gave me the sense that they had worried about her.

---

* 'Good luck' in Estonian.

Over the past few years Epp had been to countless number of countries. I bet that her family at times had no idea where she was. At any stop along the way, she could have vanished. Maybe they hoped that her wandering period was over, and a husband and baby would calm her restless soul. I felt pangs of responsibility. I was Epp's husband. I had to take care of 'their baby', even if she had never seemed like a baby to me.

Onboard, the Estonian conversations hummed quietly along. The guests stuffed their faces with the avocado and artichoke hors d'oeuvres and drank wine. After a few glasses though they actually started to stand and talk to each other. A few glasses after that, they were cracking jokes.

"We Estonians are slow to get going, but once we get going, we are hard to stop," mumbled Onu Tiit as he helped himself to more wine. Suddenly, he jogged to the back of the boat and pulled off its Estonian flag.

"Estonia is free!" he yelled, waving the flag in the air as if he were at a song festival. I was surprised. Everything about Estonian nationalism so far had seemed so serious, the wars, the deportations, why, you could even get beat up if your song didn't fare too well in the Eurovision song contest. Tiit didn't seem as if he took it so seriously. Being Estonian could be fun.

"My fellow Estonians, we are free again!" Tiit swung the flag in the air. The sound of his deep voice spread along the waters of Viljandi Lake. It climbed the hills and echoed around us. The other party guests surrounded him. Reeli wrapped her arm around her husband and helped him wave the Estonian tricolor. I put my arm around Epp.

"Estonia is free!" they all chanted. "Long live Estonia!"

AM I
PERMITTED
TO LIVE?

---

*One month after President Bush declared 'mission
accomplished' from the deck of an aircraft carrier,
a new security van entered Kentmanni Street.*

The huge vehicle with tinted windows parked directly in front
of our ground-floor apartment's window. Whenever we had the
curtains open, which was now, in summer, most of the time, we
were eye level with the van. We couldn't see the driver, but I
was pretty sure he or she could see us.

After a few days of having our private life on display, though,
we got used to it. These things just happened when you lived
across from the US Embassy. We had more important things
on our minds, such as applying for a living permit.

Epp made the appointment for me with the migration office
to discuss my case and get the required paper work, but I went
alone to sort out my status. She went to the doctor for a checkup.

It was a cloudy, humid June day in Tallinn. It was impossible to dress appropriately for the weather. The morning was

cold, so I put on corduroy pants and a light jacket. By 11 o'clock, my shirt was wet with sweat.

I walked past a statue of a man in a cape on hill, turned past the national library, found the right building, entered, and got in line to see the official. The man ahead of me had dark hair, brown eyes, and wore a navy blue pullover. He looked at me and nodded when I joined the line. He had to be a foreigner. Not only was he at the migration office, he acknowledged my existence in public and smiled.

"It's bloody humid today, ain't it? I'm sweatin' my bollocks off," he said in a British accent.

"I know, but it was cold this morning."

"Perfectly Estonian weather," he grumbled.

"So, what do we do? We just wait here and then..."

"Then you get to talk to the official. Not like you'd want to. These people are colder than a walrus' prick."

Like British people are any better, I thought of saying. Instead I said, "Yeah, I know what you mean."

"My name's John," he said, extending his hand.

"Justin," I shook his hand. "Is this your first time here?"

He shook his head. "I feel like I live in this place. I run a bar in the Old Town. Again, I've got to renew my permit. I've even got to get another bloody HIV test to do it."

"*HIV test?*"

I had only had one HIV test before, when I was in college. Giving them a blood sample was no problem. But I could barely sleep for the three days it took to find out what was my result. How well did I *really* know my ex-girlfriends? Were all the needles my doctors used *really* clean?

On judgment day, we waited in the hall at the university clinic in Washington, where we were called in one by one. There were two nurses in the room, one to tell you your result and the other to provide counseling. One girl was black, the other white. Both were young and pretty, but it was kind of hard to find someone attractive when you're getting the results of an HIV test.

I was hoping that the pretty nurses would smile and pat me on the back when I entered. Instead each looked as if someone had died.

"Justin," the nurse gripped my hand. "We have the results of your test."

"And?"

"You are HIV negative," she sighed.

It took a second to process the words. The way she said it, it sounded as if she was telling me I was positive. But I clearly heard her say I was negative.

"Wait, I'm negative?"

"Yes," she was sullen.

"That's great!"

Neither nurse shared my joy. Instead one gave me a bag filled with flavored condoms and lubricants. The other reminded me to always practice safe sex.

"You can always get more condoms and lube from us if you run out," the black nurse said.

"Was anybody positive?" I asked them on the way out the door.

The nurse rubbed her eyes. "Yeah," she said.

I realized she had a really tough job.

That had been four years ago I didn't particularly feel like reliving the experience.

"I know, I know, nothing like a good old A I D S test to ruin your week," John said after reading my expression. "But what really bugs me about these people is that they can barely speak English. They need to get with the program."

"Well, we *are* in Estonia."

"So?"

"They don't expect the officials in London to speak Estonian, do they?"

"That ain't the same thing, mate," John furrowed his brows. "It's totally different."

❋ ❋ ❋

The migration board official was a woman with sharp blue eyes. She had long legs and reminded me of a crane. She looked as if she had dealt with more desperate cases than mine.

"Fill these out and return them in three days," she sighed, handing me a packet of papers.

"Why three days? I could hand them in tomorrow."

"That's how long it will take for you to get your insurance set up. The state mandates that you be insured before we can give you a living permit. I think they can turnover an HIV test in two days if you get it done today."

I hadn't had any health insurance the entire time I had been in Estonia; I didn't think I could afford it. Now I would have to pay to set up an account with a private insurer so I could be apply for a living permit and stay with my wife.

I put the papers in my bag. "Do you think they'll let me stay? My wife is expecting a baby." I looked the woman in the eyes. Male bureaucrats might be cruel, but a female bureaucrat might have some compassion for a young family.

"I have spoken with your wife and I am familiar with your case," she said. "I'll see what we can do."

※ ※ ※

"Where were you? We agreed to meet at noon!"

Epp had been sitting alone in the cafeteria on Maakri Street for 23 minutes before her slow-walking husband showed up.

"I'm sorry," I said, sitting down at the table. "The line at the office was kind of long. I had to wait a long time before I could see the official."

"What did she say?"

"I have to fill out some forms and get insurance. I also have to get some tests done," I cracked my knuckles.

"What tests?"

"An HIV test."

"Oh, I think they just tested me for that too. They do it for every pregnant woman"

"And what was your result?" I noticed my hands shook a little as I pulled the paperwork out of my bag.

"I won't know the results until tomorrow," Epp said and sipped her cranberry juice. "Why are you acting so weird? Is something wrong?"

"I'm not acting weird."

"You haven't been able to sit straight since you sat down. And you keep fidgeting with your ring. Are you nervous about something?"

"No. Are you?"

"It's about the HIV test, isn't it?"

"How did you know?"

"The spirits told me."

I sighed.

"Have you ever had an HIV test before?" Epp sounded a little worried now, too.

"Four years ago."

"And you haven't had one since?"

"No. It's not a lot of fun."

"But all your ex-girlfriends are healthy, right?"

"As far as I know."

"And you have never used heroin or had sex with men?"

"Of course not!"

"But you're afraid you have it?"

"You never know."

"You are *so* illogical," Epp said in her all-knowing northern woman voice.

"That's not the point. Not all fears are rational."

"Do you know what the chances are that you have it?"

"Not everybody is as logical as you." I threw my utensils on the tray.

A few other diners briefly looked at us, but I had a feeling that lovers' quarrels were a regular occurrence at the cafeteria of the magazines' publishing house. The same building housed the offices of several publications run mostly by women.

"Justin, please calm down. Other people are looking at us."
She felt around in her purse and pulled out a small envelope.

"I have something from the doctor's visit," she said, handing it to me.

I opened it. There was a grainy black and white photo and floating in the center, a tiny person. The person had four small extremities and an enormous head. Its profile reminded me of Epp.

"It's a girl, she looks just like you," I said. Here she was, the future generation in an ultrasound photo. I took a bite of a potato. For a precious few moments, the living permit, the HIV test, and the big party my mom was planning in America did not exist.

"The doctor says it's too early to tell," Epp said. "I still think it's a boy."

"We'll see," I grabbed her hand.

"You shouldn't worry so much," Epp said. "I'm sure you, me, and the baby are fine."

❋ ❋ ❋

Later that afternoon I boarded a bus for the one clinic in Kristiine that could turn around an HIV test in two days. It was Wednesday and I had to submit my application for a living permit by Friday. We both had flights to New York leaving over the weekend. Epp tried to book a seat on my flight, but it was too expensive. Since we had to save every kroon we had, she got a last minute deal on a separate flight instead.

After lunch, we went to the insurance firm to open my account. All that was left to do was get the HIV test out of the way and I would be insured. With proof of the contract, I could submit my paper work, and learn my fate.

The bus left me off near a supermarket, and I found my way around a corner to a cream-colored Stalin-era building where they informed people whether they would die due to an incurable sexually-transmitted disease or live to die some other way. The office was crowded and warm. There was no air conditioning. I told the lady at the desk that I would need an HIV test. I paid her 300 precious kroons and she gave me a sheet of paper to give the nurse when my name was called.

I sat down next to a guy with a purple Mohawk. He had a nose ring. Both arms were covered in tattoos. I eyed his sheet of paper. He would be getting tested for HIV and Hepatitis C.

I looked at the punk rocker and his Mohawk and wondered if he had anything. Had he used heroin or had sex with men? Maybe he had one of his tattoos done with a dirty needle or had a condom break on him. The punk rocker looked at me, the long-haired hippie beside him, and probably thought the same things.

The nurse called me into the office. I sat in a chair and gave her a few vials of blood. She gave me a cotton swab to stop the bleeding and told me to come back on Friday morning.

I didn't sleep well that night. Logic dictated that Epp and I were fine, but logic was more persuasive during the afternoon than at 2 am. Instead I thought of all the different women from my past and what they might have forgotten to tell me.

"What's up?" Epp turned to me.

"I can't sleep."

"Are you still worried about that stupid test?"

"Yes."

"I remember my friend Kati once hooked up with a guy in Tartu. He seemed so normal. Then she found out he had been a big junkie. She was scared too."

"Did she get tested?"

"She was so nervous she said she couldn't even eat for the 48 hours it took to get her tests results."

"And?"

"She was negative, silly. I told you, we're fine. Go back to sleep."

Epp returned home from the doctor's at precisely 5:55 pm the next day, just in time for *The Bold and the Beautiful*.

In the Estonian version, Ridge and Taylor were still trying to get their kidnapped twin daughters back. In the Finnish version, though, we followed the saga of Tony Dominguez, a rising Latino fashion designer who was romantically linked with Ridge's sister and whose ex-girlfriend had just died of AIDS.

For weeks, Tony had obsessed over his status. He kept trying to tell himself that he felt fine and the chances were still good that he was clean. He didn't need to get tested.

I was in the kitchen boiling a box of *Gruusia hinkaalid*, my new favorite food, the best-tasting meat dumplings available at the corner store, when Epp came in.

"So, how was your day?" I asked.

"Good. Listen, I think we should go to the Estonian islands Hiiumaa and Saaremaa when we get back in August," she said. "The magazine wants me to interview some people there."

"And did you see the doctor?"

"Yeah. Listen, I was already thinking about how we would go to the islands. It's possible to fly there or take a ferry. What do you think?"

"Epp, but what was your test result?"

"Oh, that. Of course, I'm fine."

"You're fine?"

"See for yourself." She handed me the printout of her blood workup. She was telling the truth. She was fine, no HIV.

"You're kind of a hypochondriac," she said. She filled a bowl with fruits and settled down for the saxophone-driven theme song to our evening show.

We ate dinner together and waited to see if Tony Dominguez was negative or if he had HIV. "Are you still nervous about getting your results tomorrow?" she said during a commercial break.

"No. I don't care what happens to me. As long as you and the baby are alright, then I have nothing to worry about."

Deep inside, I realized that baby's life would go on, even if I was sentenced to die. I found the thought comforting.

❋ ❋ ❋

I passed the punk rocker on the way up the steps to the clinic in Kristiine. He was wearing sunglasses. I couldn't tell if his test results were good or bad.

At the desk inside, I gave them my name. It was still humid, except now they had installed a fan. The woman behind the counter opened up a folder and handed me a scrap of paper. I went and sat down and waited for them to call me.

After 15 minutes, I got impatient.

"When will the nurse see me to discuss my results?" I asked the woman.

"What? Why are you still here? Your results are right there," she pointed to the sheet of paper I had held for the last 15 minutes. I scanned through the short text and found the word I had been looking for.

Negatiivne.

I was relieved and a little confused. Where was the nurse? Where was my counselor? Where was my free bag of lubricants and flavored condoms?

And if you were positive, did the Estonians inform you the same way, with a little slip of paper?

I took a cab to the migration office where this time there was no line. The official received my paperwork. She was unsure of what they would decide, given the fact that I had been in their country illegally for a month and a half. I told her again of our baby. She said again she would do her best.

Epp's flight to New York would take her via Warsaw where she would spend the night with Dorota, a Polish journalist from our Finnish correspondents' program. My flight would leave the next day. We would land in New York within half an hour of each other on Sunday afternoon.

"I hope everything will work out with your living permit," Epp said as she waited to check in at the airport. "Did she say when it would be ready?"

"When the official called, she said the actual card will be ready in a week, but the biggest problem is that we won't be here. I won't have it when I come back in August. Hopefully, they'll put me in the system so that border security will know they can let me in."

"I'm sure they will."

"I hope so, too."

"Maybe we should have gotten married in May," she said. "If we hadn't listened to that witch Anna, then we would have married a month before, and you would have your living permit already." Epp frowned.

"But it was bad luck to get married in May. She said we'd have better luck if we got married in June."

I walked Epp to security and kissed her goodbye. She waved as she went through the metal detectors. Right before she passed passport control, she blew me a big kiss. Then she was gone.

When Epp and I parted in Heathrow the November before, it brought me to tears. At that point, we weren't sure when would we meet next. Now I only had about 36 hours to spend alone. I didn't cry, but I felt empty.

There was nothing to do in our apartment. I decided to walk through the Old Town. The teenage girls were still selling postcards and roasted nuts. The Scandinavian tourists were still out drinking beers in the cafes. Everyone seemed content. To them, I was just another stranger, another tiny speck of unknown humanity on the surface of the earth. I stood before St. Olaf's Church and looked up. A year before Tallinn had seemed so magical; now it was just a bunch of old buildings.

In the Estonian Russian Internet café, I checked my e-mail. Epp had written me from Warsaw. She was with Dorota now, but everything was not fine.

It was so hot in the Warsaw airport I fainted. They took me to the doctor there and I had to lie with the IV for two hours. He said the baby should be ok.

I wanted to be with her and help, but she was hundreds of miles away. I didn't even have Dorota's phone number where I could reach her. All I could do is write back and tell her I loved her.

I went home, ate another box of meat dumplings. I even watched *The Bold and the Beautiful* because I knew that Epp would want to know what happened next on the show.

Ridge's sister finally persuaded Tony Dominguez to see a doctor. She assured him that everything was ok. At the end of the show the doctor entered the room and told Tony that he was HIV positive. He was not as lucky as me.

I packed my bags and looked around our tiny apartment. Would this be the last time I spent the night in this place? Would they let me back in the country? Or not? I curled up alone on my side of the bed and tried to sleep.

"You are beyond the 90-day limit," the Estonian passport control officer shook her head. Her red hair hung down in braids. She wore glasses and a uniform. "I have to call my boss."

"No, there must be some mistake," I told her. It was the morning of my flight out to Helsinki. From there I would connect to New York. "I have a permit."

"Can I see it?"

"I don't have it with me. It was just granted."

"Well, it's not in the database."

"I just got the approval on Friday afternoon. Maybe they didn't have time to put it in the system."

The officer called her boss. A thin blond man with a moustache appeared from behind a door.

"You are in a lot of trouble," he said as he walked me to a table in the airport's café. It was early morning. There were barely any other travelers around. "You'll have to fill out a form explaining why you overstayed."

"What do you mean, 'a lot of trouble'?"

"I mean you can't come back, at least this year."

"But I have a living permit."

"Not according to our database."

He handed me a sheet of paper. I wondered what a guy like Rick, that savvy expat who was thinking of dumping Tallinn for Kiev, would do in a situation like this. My hands were shaky, but I wrote in passable Estonian about our marriage and the coming of the *tita**. The officer read it over and played with his moustache.

---

* 'Baby' in Estonian.

"*Tita?*" he looked me in the eyes. "Your wife is pregnant?"

"Yes, she's expecting a little *tita.*"

He tried to remain reserved, but his steely blue eyes were suddenly moist. It was almost as if he wanted to say, 'you're going to have a little *tita*? *Tita*s are the most adorable things in the world!'

"There's one more thing," the officer suddenly regained his interrogator's composure.

"What?"

He pushed the paper across the table and pointed a bony finger at a vacant box.

"You forgot to write your passport number."

ESTONIAN
HOUSE

"Give me a scoop of chocolate and a scoop of vanilla with extra sprinkles and chocolate syrup. Give me an extra-large coffee, light and sweet, and a box of those Krispy Kreme donuts."

The train got us into New York's Penn Station at 11 am. It was a breezy Saturday in July. The train terminal was crowded with people who wanted to spend a rare cool summer day in Manhattan. We had been in New York for almost a month. The wedding blessing was a week away.

Now we were standing in front of a crowd of people waiting for the bald fat guy in the New York Yankees t-shirt ahead of us to finish placing his order. All we wanted to buy were two coffees. But Epp and I wound up eating ice cream and donuts for breakfast, too. When in America, do as the Americans.

"I am getting really tired of this bullshit," I told her as the guy behind the counter handed us our breakfast in waffle cones. "I am tired of people criticizing me."

"Why are they criticizing you?"

"I haven't been a good boy."

"Are you still upset over what Rose said?" she asked. Rose was my friend Becky's mom. She had known me since junior high school and had been on the same morning train as us.

"Well you heard her. I went up to see Becky and her at the Beach Club, and she said everybody started ripping me apart as soon as we left."

"It wasn't everybody. It was that woman."

"She said it was Michelle Diamond. Her son was the star basketball player in high school. He's in law school."

"What did she say that was so bad?"

"She said only people from Alabama have children at our age."

"But I am almost 29. You are almost 24. I don't understand."

"It doesn't matter how old we really are. It matters how much money we have. Since we're not wealthy, they think of us as teenagers."

"Listen, it was just one random woman who said something bad about you. There's no reason for it to ruin our day. She's just some suburban housewife. She doesn't know who we are."

"Mom was the same age as me when my brother was born. Her father was the same age as me when my mom was born. Why do I feel like a foreigner in my own country?"

"We'll be back in Estonia in a couple of weeks," Epp said as we took the escalators up into Midtown. "Then we don't have to worry about being teenage parents."

❀ ❀ ❀

New York's Estonian House was located on East 34th Street. To get there you had to walk by the Empire State Building. It was still morning and the line to get inside New York's tallest building already wrapped around the corner. We walked by the tourists and the street sloped down into a quiet neighborhood of convenience stores, apartment buildings, and restaurants.

The Estonian House was a modest building downwind of skyscrapers. The Estonians bought it in 1946 and never let go. No matter who you were, if you were in New York and Estonian, or even just married to one, you were welcome in the Estonian House.

Epp and I had been inside the house before Christmas when Epp visited New York for the first time. No matter what time of day it was, it was always dark inside. Black and white photos of emotionless Estonians of the 1930s were framed in the main corridor. An Estonian flag and an American flag hung near the entrance. Looking down on it all was a somber portrait of Estonia's president, Konstantin Päts. It was almost like a time capsule from the 1930s.

We arrived at the building and sat on its steps. Epp buzzed the door, but no one answered. It was a minute to noon. Within seconds, Jürgen, the 29-year-old new president of the New York Estonian Educational Society, was supposed to show up for an interview.

Five minutes passed. Then 10 minutes. Jürgen was now really late for his appointment. How un-Estonian of him.

"Where could he be?" I asked. "He's 20 minutes late."

349

"Late people are assholes." Epp said. "Now you know why it's good to be on time."

She had a point. Maybe there was something to punctuality after all.

At last, 27 minutes after our agreed upon appointment, a yellow taxi pulled up, and a tall man jumped out and approached us.

"Sorry I'm late, I'm Jürgen," he said, scratching his nose. With his black light-weight coat and long cotton scarf, he looked like a movie star.

"That's alright," I said. "I am always late."

"My mother-in-law's in town. I had my hands full this morning."

"I guess you have the key to the house?" I asked.

"I don't want to be indoors on a day like today. I know an open-air café nearby. We can go there and talk."

❊ ❊ ❊

Jürgen was well-dressed for a casual Saturday morning. Under his coat and scarf, he wore a button-down white shirt and dress pants. His short brown hair looked as if it had just been cut, his long face just shaved. In every way, he was a professional as he ordered a cup of coffee from a waiter. He was the leader of the New York Estonians.

I came here to interview him about his role as their new president for the *Baltic Times*. He said the Estonian House was a "sinking ship." It was in dire financial trouble due, ironically, to the existence of an independent Estonian state.

"Before 1991, when an old Estonian with a big estate died in New York, he would leave part of it to the Estonian House. He had to, there was no other foundation to which he could contribute," Jürgen said. "These days, when an old Estonian dies, he leaves it to some foundation in Estonia. We're now running out of the old money and they need to get some new money fast. That's why they hired me."

"Why? What do you know about money?"

"I'm a quant."

"A quant?"

"A quantitative analyst. I help investment companies build mathematical models for risk management and things like that."

"Where did you learn how to be a quant?"

"Harvard." He leaned in for another sip of coffee. I could see the Chrysler Building behind him.

Jürgen left Estonia when he was a teenager. First he moved to Finland with his mother, later to Connecticut on a basketball scholarship. But Jürgen wasn't just a good ball player. He was an Ivy League scholar and now a Wall Street number cruncher that was paid handsomely for his work.

"That's all you do in New York," he said. "You just make money. You have an apartment where you sleep. Usually this apartment has a shoebox-size kitchen, but you never eat there, you only need to keep your water bottle there, because you're always eating lunch at the office and dinner at the office or at a restaurant. You earn money all week and then you spend it all weekend at restaurants and bars and clubs and parties."

I realized that Jürgen had taken the life path I was supposed to follow. I was supposed to leave college and get a prestigious

New York job, a roomy apartment, and a salary I blew at clubs on the weekend because that's what young people were supposed to do. Sure, he married his college sweetheart, a Harvard graduate, at a relatively young age, but at least they didn't have any children, so, basically, they were normal.

"New York isn't America," he explained. "It's filled with people like me from all over the world. We work hard, and we party hard. Everyone tries to put a little money aside so that one day when they get old they can get out."

My article was supposed to be about the Estonian House, but now it seemed as if it would also be about its charismatic leader. The Estonian community in New York had changed. It wasn't just old farts toasting to President Päts. There was fresh, post-91 blood.

"So what do you plan to do with the Estonian House?"

"We're thinking of selling the air rights."

"Air rights?"

"We own the air above the building. Technically, we could sell the air rights to a developer who could build a skyscraper around us." He took another sip of coffee.

I tried to imagine the three-story modest building with a skyscraper sitting on it. I couldn't.

"What about the community, is it dying out or are there more Estonians coming?" I asked.

"There's a steady trickle. And whenever a new Estonian shows up in town, they can come to me and I can help them find a job," he said.

"On Wall Street?"

"Anywhere," he leaned in closer. "I have connections."

"Tell me more about your wife. How did you meet?" Epp asked. She was writing a feature for the woman's magazine where she worked, about Jürgen's personal life. I imagined that many of her readers might consider such a man a catch. They switched into Estonian, and I realized my part of the interview was over.

"Look, my friend Eamon just sent me a text message. He and some friends are in Central Park," I told them.

"That's ok," Epp said. "I have some other interviews to do. Let's try to meet up by 5."

I opened my wallet to leave money for the coffee.

"No, no, that's fine," Jürgen held up his hands. "It's all on me."

I got off the subway train on East 68th street and couldn't move. The track platforms and escalators were choked with people. Similar throngs filled the sunny streets. There were couples on rollerblades and gangs of college kids; even one of those South American pan-flute groups playing ABBA's greatest hits. It felt good to be back in the center of New York's carnival of life, but how was I supposed to find Eamon here?

I elbowed my way through the people – mostly young, mostly white – to Central Park. I was about to dial Eamon's number, when I saw three guys in Yankees hats strutting my way.

"What's up, man? Long time no see," Eamon grinned as he approached me. He was flanked by two guys I had never met before. With freckles and red hair, they looked to be just as

Irish and Catholic as Eamon was. All of them held 2-liter coke bottles in their hands.

"This is Jimmy and this is Sean," Eamon introduced his friends.

"Why are all these people here?" I asked.

"There's a big hip hop concert in the park," Eamon said. "The rumor is that De La Soul is going to show up. Q-Tip from A Tribe Called Quest might be there too."

"Do you have tickets?"

"They're playing in the amphitheater, so you can hear the concert if you are nearby. We don't need tickets, we can just camp behind the stage," Jimmy said. "That's what all these other people are probably going to do."

We walked into the park. Young half-naked tanned bodies – some male, some female – were strewn sunbathing across its lawns like seals. They all wore bottoms, but few had on tops.

"Oh my God, did you see that chick? She had the biggest tits," Eamon motioned towards one of the sun bathers as he drank from his coke bottle. "Wouldn't it be nice if instead of shaking a girl's hand, you could just feel her up?"

"Don't you have a girlfriend?" I asked Eamon.

"Sorry, man," he said. "I forgot you're married. You know I haven't gotten laid for, like, a week because Michelle didn't want to come down from Boston this weekend."

Michelle was Eamon's girlfriend. They didn't live together, but he liked her enough that he had moved to Boston to be near her after we graduated from college in Washington. Still, most of his friends were in New York. He was in constant movement between the two cities.

Eamon had majored in English, but found himself waiting tables instead.

"Did I tell you I waited on Natalie Portman?" he asked.

"Who's that?"

"She plays Queen Amidala in the new *Star Wars* movies. She's totally hot, but she barely gave me a fucking tip."

"How's your job?"

"It's ok, but there are a lot Mexicans working in the kitchen. Most of them don't even speak English. They are all illegal."

"You want to know something funny? I'm illegal in Estonia."

"No shit! So you can't go back there?"

"They told me I had a permit, but at the airport they told me I wasn't in the system. I don't know what's going to happen."

"Good luck, man."

"Did you see any vendors recently?" I asked. "I'm really thirsty."

"Here," Eamon handed over his bottle. "Drink up."

I took a sip from the bottle. It was warm and sweet and spiked with Tennessee whiskey.

"Hmm, this doesn't taste just like Coke," I said as I felt the first drops of alcohol buzz.

"You can finish it, man," Eamon said. "Sean's got another one in his bag."

"Why don't you guys just drink beer?"

"You can't drink beer in Central Park!" Eamon said. "Mayor Giuliani put an end to that stuff years ago. I got caught once with an open container. Luckily the cop wasn't a dick so he let me off."

We sat on the grass near the amphitheater where, according to the rumors, famous New York hip hop groups were poised to play. I drank around a quarter of the container and handed it back to Eamon. We waited and waited but never heard any music. By about half past 4, we decided to give up. Eamon, Sean, and Jimmy had finished their Coke bottles too.

"Ok, this place sucks," Eamon slurred. "Plus we're out of booze."

"There's a liquor store over on East 66th," Sean said. "We can fuel up there."

"Sorry guys, but I've got to split," I said.

"*Come on*, it's not even 5 o'clock!" Eamon whined.

"I'm supposed to meet Epp at 5."

"So what? *She* can wait. Drink with us. Don't be such a fucking pussy, man."

"I'm not a fucking pussy!"

"Really?"

"She's pregnant. She needs my help."

"Ok, ok, that's cool," Eamon said. "Go be with your wife and I'll catch you at the wedding blessing thing."

"I'll walk you guys to the liquor store," I said. It seemed like a friendly compromise.

There were now fewer people at the entrance to Central Park. If the concert did go on, it would probably be later.

"I need to tell you that I'm really proud of you, man," Eamon said as I left him and the boys at the door to the liquor store. "You're married and you're going to be a father. I could never handle that."

"Sure you could," I said. "I'll see you and Michelle at the party next week."

Epp ordered an enchilada. I ordered a chimichanga. She said summer in Manhattan was dirty and humid. It reminded her of Spain. We decided to get dinner at a Mexican restaurant near the Estonian House to take advantage of the city's southern ambiance.

Epp had actually been sitting at this restaurant since Jürgen left her hours ago. Throughout the day, she had interviewed different people. Now, sitting across from each other at a table on the sidewalk, we were as alone as two people could be in New York.

"So how was Eamon?" she asked.

"The same."

The waitress brought us our drinks.

"It's so good to be here away from all the party planning," she sipped her juice. "I know I shouldn't say it, but, I can't wait until it's all over."

"That's what I'm waiting for. I can't wait until Sunday night, when I shake the last person's hand at the party, get back to the house, tear the tux off my body, and slide into a t-shirt and jeans..."

"Oh," Epp interrupted me. "Did I tell you that I checked my e-mail this morning and I got an answer back from the migration board."

"Why didn't you tell me?"

"I was so busy preparing for these interviews."

"What did they say?"

"They said your new identity card is waiting for you in the Hansapank office in Old Town."

"But how can I pick it up if they don't let me into the country?"

"I don't know. We need to mail them back and ask."

"It's so frustrating. I mean we are blocks from the Estonian consulate here. They could technically give me one. But they are not allowed to do it, I guess."

"What would you do if they actually didn't let you in?"

"I'd find a way in."

"How?"

"I'd commandeer a fishing boat out of Kotka and have them drop me off somewhere on the north coast at night. Then I'd hitchhike to Tallinn."

"What if they caught you?"

"I'd disguise myself as an Estonian. I'd bleach my hair and get blue contact lenses."

"Did you have anything to drink while you were with Eamon?"

"Not really."

"Ha. I knew it."

The waitress brought us our food. It was still sizzling on the plates.

"Let's not think about the wedding blessing party and getting back to Estonia," I said. "We're in Manhattan tonight. Let's enjoy it."

UP
NORTH

Each time the floor moved I opened my eyes. Where am I? I looked around. Is the plane landing? I glanced out the window and saw the sea. I was on a boat.

It was the last leg of a four-part journey from New York to Tallinn. I was exhausted. The trip involved three flights and a boat ride. It was a last-minute deal. Epp had flown home via Warsaw a few days before. She was waiting for me.

I hoped that Estonian border security would not ruin our reunion.

First, though, I had to go to England. The British Airways flight left New York, flew through the night, and dropped me off in London the next morning.

"How long do you plan to stay in the United Kingdom?" a British passport control officer asked me. I had to go the baggage claim and check in again with KLM.

"About 40 minutes," I told her.

"Oh, that's fine," she smiled and waved me through.

Maybe these Britons weren't so bad after all. Maybe Epp and I could both come and study here. It might be an option should I be banned from Estonian territory.

From London I flew to Amsterdam, where I had two coffees in a smoky airport café, packed with drunken British football fans.

"What's with the long face?" a fat one said after he elbowed me in the gut while reaching for another beer.

"Nothing," I told him.

"Doesn't look like nothing," he said. "You look like you've got real problems."

In Amsterdam, I was still functional. I could safely sit in a café and fret over what might happen if I showed up in Tallinn and they didn't let me in. It was on the flight from Amsterdam to Helsinki though that I began to black out.

Most of the time, a person is either awake or asleep. On the flight to Helsinki I was so tired that I couldn't really tell at any given moment what or where I was. I drank two more coffees in the air and thought I could get through the last parts of the trip without needing any more caffeine. I would stride up to the passport check in Tallinn fully alert and hand them my documents. There would be no problems. Then I woke up with my mouth pressed against the airplane window.

Who am I? Am I who I think I am? Am I really married? Is a baby on the way? Were those really my parents? Is half a bed really waiting for me halfway across the world? Will they let me in? Or will they send me back on the border? Will I spend the night in Finland? Will I have to go back to the US? It had been a chaotic few weeks to end a chaotic year.

A year-ago to the day I had landed in the same airport, changed my pants in the restroom (I spilled red wine on them on the plane), brushed my teeth, tried to look normal, and was met by two sharply dressed, blond and blue-eyed representatives of the Finnish foreign ministry. They drove me to our dormitory – we listened to Finnish pop music the whole ride – and I collapsed into a chair in the dormitory's common room, completely unaware of the Estonian journalist who had just moved in one floor below.

"Justin, please wake up," I remember Natalie the Brit saying that day. "Everybody wants to meet you."

I forced myself awake and greeted them. It wasn't everyday that other people were actually interested in who I was.

The year of change was capped with the wedding blessing. It took place on Sunday, July 20, Epp's 29th birthday, in my hometown on Long Island. If they denied me entrance in Tallinn, we might have to go back there, though I wasn't sure if we could ever fit in.

I was informed later that the salmon at the party was delicious and the venue, a classy restaurant, a perfect choice. My mother had even arranged a horse-drawn carriage flying American and Estonian flags. Even if her son had kind of screwed up, she was going to send him off into marital life in style.

Sure, there had been some yelling, proclamations of hatred, and the occasional throwing of inanimate objects before the ceremony, a few by me. That's just how my Italian family life operated. Asked afterwards by my mother how the wedding went, I disappointed her. I could barely remember a thing.

We sat in the first pew of the old church, I remembered that. The priest was dragging on through a sermon. He had some deep thoughts on the relationship between God's love and love between a husband and wife.

"I told you this dress would be too tight by now," Epp said. "I'm really thirsty. Maybe I can go to the restroom and get a drink?"

"Don't worry," I said. "It will be over in a few minutes."

Except it wasn't, the priest kept talking and talking. Finally, we were asked to rise and approach the altar for the most important part.

I helped Epp up and she gripped my arm. She looked confused. Her eyes were open but she looked past me to the crucifix on the wall. Then she slumped over and collapsed on the floor.

There was a sea of movement around me as I leaned down to help her.

"Get her up, get her up!" someone yelled. We pulled Epp into the pew, and someone pulled flowers from a vase and dumped the water on her face.

"She's still breathing, but I need to check her tongue!" the man said, grasping her throat. I realized it was one of my parents' friends; an old neighbor who was an emergency medical technician.

A minute later, Epp started talking about angels. Her eyes were wide open but she did not seem to recognize anyone. Another minute passed and all of a sudden she sat up. She said she was fine, drank a cup of holy water someone brought her, and the ceremony continued.

Was it a bad omen that she fainted? I thought we would get through the ceremony with no problems but the gods had a way of making things more interesting. I hope they weren't conspiring to play another memorable trick on us at the Tallinn ferry terminal.

"Tea or coffee?" A hand tugged at my forearm. I remembered I was on a plane as I opened my eyes again. "I'm sorry to disturb you, sir, but would you like tea or coffee?"

"Another coffee." I must have fallen asleep again. I glanced out the windows and saw the clouds part. The familiar forests of Finland stretched out below. *Finland*, I thought, my throbbing forehead against the glass, *I'm almost home*.

❈ ❈ ❈

"Is it ok if I roll down the window? I need some air."

The cab driver looked over his shoulder and nodded.

Helsinki was cool and gray. Everything was as I had left it: clean, quiet, and efficient. The taxi driver was fat and had a moustache. He was polite but left me alone. I was grateful, because I needed to pray.

I had to be in their database. The migration board had to have informed them that I could legally enter the country. It had been a month and a half. Surely, they had updated their systems by now. I tried to convince myself that everything would be fine. Or was I deluding myself?

We drove past the train station, past Stockmann, and Helsinki's Dome Church, the *Tuomiokirkko*. I wondered if anybody else felt the same way about this place that I did. Did anybody else wait for the *Esplanaadi* to appear, peering out their car window into the afternoon air, thinking of how a certain woman once stood at the end of it, the sea behind her back?

Helsinki was different from New York. In New York, I was surrounded by dizzying smells, noise, and people; a 24-hour circus. But here up north, I was adrift on an ocean of personal space. I could breathe and be left alone. It was liberating.

The driver dropped me off at the harbor, and I called Epp from a payphone to let her know when I would be arriving.

"I'll be in at 7 o'clock tonight," I said. "Will you come meet me?"

"Of course I will," she said. "I miss you."

"I'll be there soon."

"You have to come home and sleep. We have to fly out to Hiiumaa island tomorrow morning."

I could see it happening. I would arrive at the gates. They would swipe my passport and the system would tell them I had a living permit. They would hand it back, and the next day I would be on an exotic Estonian island. It could happen. Maybe if I imagined hard enough, I could make it come true.

I bought an iced coffee from a kiosk to sustain me for the final part of my journey. Then I gave the *Esplanaadi* one last look and boarded the fast-ferry to Tallinn.

First there were islands and then there were churches. The ferry slowed as it entered Tallinn harbor. The clouds had parted and everything around me glimmered in the sunlight. I went up on deck to watch the golden city.

I could see St. Olaf's Church and Alexander Nevski Cathedral, the Olümpia hotel and the SAS Radisson hotel. Even from the deck of a ferry, I knew the way home. I knew there was a woman there waiting for me. All I had to do was get off the boat, present my passport, say a little prayer to the gods under my breath, and hope my night would end on Kentmanni Street.

Then, as the boat pulled in to dock, I saw her standing next to the glass ferry terminal. She was wearing a hooded sweatshirt, a skirt, and eating ice cream. She noticed me and smiled. From the way the light wind played with her clothes, I could see that her belly was a little bigger and it wasn't just from ice cream. I waved to her as I descended the ferry steps into the terminal building. Almost there.

I got in the line for border security and tried to relax but my hands kept shaking. I held them up to the light and tried to stop it, but I couldn't control the nervous energy that ran through my body.

The line wasn't long. There were about a dozen people ahead of me. None of them had any problems. I hoped that maybe the border security would get lazy. Maybe they would just have a look at my American passport, deem it of good quality, and wave me through, just like the British border guard in the morning.

They were now the only people who stood between me and my wife.

"Passport, please," a woman said. She wore glasses, had dark brown hair pulled back into a ponytail, and looked incredibly bored.

I handed her the document and she flipped through its pages, past the stamps for Iceland, the Danish student visa, and the blue British crown, and multiple other ones I had picked up in my short but eventful life as a traveler. The passport was due to expire in eight years. I imagined it could get full before then.

The officer ran it through a scanner. Then she stared at her computer screen.

I stood there waiting, thinking: *Just do it, take the stamp, put it in my passport, and wave me through. Just do it, just stamp the passport and let me see my wife.*

"It says you entered in January and exited in June," the officer said. "Why are you spending so much time in Estonia?"

"My wife is Estonian," I pleaded. "She is expecting a baby."

"But according to this data, you cannot enter. You stayed longer than you are allowed last time."

"But the migration board has issued me a living permit. Doesn't it say that in your database?"

"There is nothing here about a living permit," she shook her head.

"Please, my wife is waiting on the other side of that door."

"Sir..."

"They said my permit is in the Hansapank office in Old Town. Let's go there together. Let's go and get a cab and I can show you..."

"Sir, I'm afraid..."

"No, I'm not going anywhere!" I cried out. "You are not going to keep us apart."

"Sir, I need to speak to my boss," the officer took off her glasses. "It should take about four minutes."

The officer stood up and went into another room. I imagined they were arguing inside on whether or not to send me back to Finland.

Ten minutes later she emerged. I tried to read her for any sign of emotion – would they let me stay or would I have to hijack a boat out of Kotka tonight? She still looked glazed over.

"My boss has called the migration board," she said. "This was very hard for us to do, as it is after hours."

"Ok."

"He spoke to an official there and they reviewed your information."

"And?"

"And you were right, sir. You do have a living permit. You will be permitted to enter the country."

I exhaled and rubbed my face. Then I ran my hands through my hair and pulled on it a little to relieve the stress. I closed my eyes for a second while I did it, and in that second I could have fallen asleep.

"Sir?"

I opened my eyes. "I'm sorry. It's been a long day, night; it's just been a really long trip."

She stamped my passport and handed it back to me. Then she nodded to the person behind me, signaling that I could go.

❀ ❀ ❀

On the other side of the door, Epp and I hugged and kissed. She even allowed me a bite of her ice cream.

"It took so long, I knew you were having trouble so I went and knocked on their door and told them your story," Epp said. "They were really stubborn. It looked almost like I had to call the migration board myself but finally I made them call."

"I don't even want to think about it anymore," I wrapped my arm around her. "Let's just go home."